family flip QUIZ

The questions are divided into nine subjects: General Knowledge, Geography, Natural World, History, Science and Maths, English, Sport, T.V. and Film and Music. You should attempt all questions though.

As you progress through the quizzes you will notice that the questions get a little harder. We think the easiest level is level 1 and the hardest is level 4, but you may find it the other way round. It all depends on what you happen to know.

This is how to use your *Flip Quiz*: if you are answering questions on your own just cover the answers with your hand or a piece of card. You may want to write down your answers and count up your scores for each quiz.

If you are doing the quizzes with a partner or in teams, unfold the base and stand the *Flip Quiz* on a flat surface between you and your partner. Read aloud the questions (but not the answers!) and allow your partner to say the answers or write them down. You may answer each question in turn or answer an entire quiz in turn. Keep your scores on a piece of paper and compare results.

The illustrations are there to help you get the right answers when competing with a partner. For instance, if you are answering Quiz 1 questions, you will be looking at and reading out Quiz 2. However, the illustrations you will see are clues to help you do Quiz 1. Look at the labels by the illustrations. These tell you which question they are clues for. The illustrations at the head of each quiz are an additional picture clue.

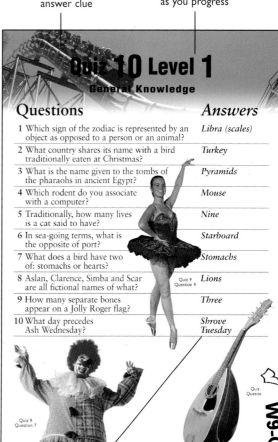

Quiz 10 Level 1
General Knowledge

Questions	Answers
1 Which sign of the zodiac is represented by an object as opposed to a person or an animal?	Libra (scales)
2 What country shares its name with a bird traditionally eaten at Christmas?	Turkey
3 What is the name given to the tombs of the pharaohs in ancient Egypt?	Pyramids
4 Which rodent do you associate with a computer?	Mouse
5 Traditionally, how many lives is a cat said to have?	Nine
6 In sea-going terms, what is the opposite of port?	Starboard
7 What does a bird have two of: stomachs or hearts?	Stomachs
8 Aslan, Clarence, Simba and Scar are all fictional names of what?	Lions
9 How many separate bones appear on a Jolly Roger flag?	Three
10 What day precedes Ash Wednesday?	Shrove Tuesday

Quiz 9 Question 9

Quiz 9 Question 7

Quiz Questio

W9-CAI-431

Questions	Answers
1 Which arch-enemy of Peter Pan was played by Dustin Hoffman on film?	*Captain Hook*
2 Who wrote *The Wind in the Willows*?	*Kenneth Grahame*
3 What are the short pleated skirts associated with Scotland called?	*Kilts*
4 Is the word no negative or positive?	*Negative*
5 Which wimple wearers live in convents?	*Nuns*
6 What does a frogman wear on his feet?	*Flippers*
7 What is the name of the largest castle in the capital city of Scotland?	*Edinburgh Castle*
8 What name is given to a 60th part of an hour?	*A minute*
9 What kind of animal is Brian in *The Magic Roundabout*?	*A snail*
10 What part of the body is treated by an optician?	*The eyes*

Quiz 2
Question 9

Quiz 2
Question 8

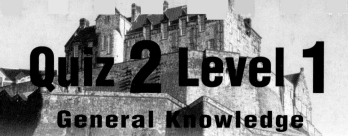

Quiz 2 Level 1

General Knowledge

Questions	Answers
1 What part of the body is treated by a chiropodist?	*Feet*
2 Which biblical trio bore gifts of gold, frankincense and myrrh?	*Three Wise Men*
3 If someone is descending are they going up or down?	*Down*
4 By what title is the Bishop of Rome also known?	*The Pope*
5 On which temperature scale is 212 degrees the boiling point of water?	*Fahrenheit*
6 What name is given to the heavy implement used to moor a sailing boat to the sea bed?	*Anchor*
7 Which television street featured the characters of Bert, Ernie and the Cookie Monster?	**Sesame Street**
8 What is the children's section of Penguin books called?	*Puffin*
9 What is the Italian word for pie?	*Pizza*
10 What type of creatures live in an aquarium?	*Fish*

Quiz 1
Question 9

Quiz 1
Question 1

Quiz 3 Level 1

Natural World

Questions	Answers
1 Would you expect to see a gudgeon flying, swimming, or burrowing?	*Swimming (it is a type of fish)*
2 What is the name of the sweet liquid collected from flowers by bees?	*Nectar*
3 Long-eared, snowy and barn are all species of which nocturnal bird?	*Owl*
4 What breed of dogs are Bull, Airedale and Yorkshire?	*Terriers*
5 What four-letter word is the name given to the home of a wolf?	*Lair*
6 True or false: a giraffe has the same number of neck bones as a human?	*True (both have seven)*
7 How many humps does a Bactrian camel have?	*Two*
8 What is the largest member of the cat family?	*Tiger*
9 How many legs does a starfish have?	*Five*
10 Do reptiles have warm or cold blood?	*Cold*

Quiz 4
Question 3

Quiz 4 Level 1
Natural World

Questions	Answers
1 What sea creature possesses three hearts and eight tentacles?	*Octopus*
2 What short slang word for a child is also the name for a young goat?	*Kid*
3 What does a caterpillar evolve into before taking flight?	*Butterfly*
4 What is the national flower of Wales?	*Daffodil*
5 Are tigers native to Africa or Asia?	*Asia*
6 Which amphibian hosts the *Muppet Show*?	*Kermit the Frog*
7 Anaconda and cobra are both species of what?	*Snake*
8 What four-letter word connects a dollar and a male rabbit?	*Buck*
9 The leaves of the eucalyptus tree are the staple diet of which Australian marsupial?	*Koala bear*
10 How many teeth does an aardvark have?	*None*

Quiz 3
Question 3

Quiz 3
Question 8

Quiz 5 Level 1
General Knowledge

Questions	Answers
1 The star sign of Gemini is represented by a pair of what?	*Twins*
2 What seven-letter H word is the name of a leather case for holding a pistol or revolver?	*Holster*
3 How many meanings does a *double entendre* have?	*Two*
4 What do you call the tall, decorated wooden pillars carved by Native Americans?	*Totem poles*
5 Which alcoholic drink is also the name given to the left side of a ship?	*Port*
6 What is the American equivalent of a Russian cosmonaut?	*Astronaut*
7 What instrument is named after the Greek god Pan?	*Pan pipes*
8 Nag is a slang term for what animal?	*Horse*
9 What type of weapon is a cutlass?	*A short curved sword*
10 What type of boat is steered by a gondolier?	*Gondola*

Quiz 6
Question 5

Quiz 6
Question 2

Quiz 6 Level 1

General Knowledge

Questions	Answers
1 In the nursery rhyme, who lost her sheep?	*Little Bo Peep*
2 Which musical instrument has 47 strings and 7 pedals?	*Harp*
3 What type of dish is cock-a-leekie?	*Soup*
4 Who wrote the *Secret Seven* books?	*Enid Blyton*
5 What is the national flower of Holland?	*Tulip*
6 In the fairytale, who scaled a giant beanstalk and battled with a giant?	*Jack*
7 Which international competition, has been won by Abba and Katrina and the Waves?	*Eurovision Song Contest*
8 In which city does the Scottish Parliament meet?	*Edinburgh*
9 Which of the Teletubbies rides a scooter?	*Po*
10 What kind of animal is Disney's Dumbo?	*Elephant*

Quiz 5
Question 4

Quiz 5
Question 7

Quiz 7 Level 1

History

Questions	Answers
1 In which decade did World War II begin?	*1930s (1939-1945)*
2 Who in 1911 was the first man to reach the South Pole?	*Roald Amundsen*
3 Name the fleet sent by Philip II of Spain against England in 1588?	*Spanish Armada*
4 How many British Kings have been called George?	*Six*
5 What were the followers of Oliver Cromwell called?	*Roundheads*
6 Which mountain did Edward Wymper climb in 1869?	*The Matterhorn*
7 "Watson come here, I want you" were the first ever words spoken on the what?	*Telephone*
8 Which American President was assassinated in November 1963?	*John F. Kennedy*
9 According to the Bible which sea did Moses part the waves of?	*Red Sea*
10 Which British Queen died in 1901?	*Queen Victoria*

Quiz 8
Question 9

Quiz 8
Question 5

HAROLD

Quiz 8 Level 1
History

Questions	Answers
1 In mythology, whose face was said to have launched a thousand ships?	*Helen of Troy*
2 What was built in 122A.D. to separate the lands of the Britons and the Picts?	*Hadrian's Wall*
3 Which country opened its first underground railway in 1904?	*United States*
4 What was the first name of the Scottish king known as *The Bruce*?	*Robert*
5 Which famous tapestry depicts the Battle of Hastings?	*Bayeaux Tapestry*
6 When was the Panama Canal formally opened?	*1920*
7 Was the 1940 Battle of Britain fought on land, at sea or in the air?	*In the air*
8 Who disappeared during a flight across the Pacific in 1937?	*Amelia Earhart*
9 What vegetable is Walter Raleigh credited with introducing to Britain?	*Potato*
10 Which King of Wessex was said to have burnt the cakes of a swineherd's wife?	*Alfred the Great*

Quiz 7
Question 5

Quiz 7
Question 3

Quiz 9 Level 1
General Knowledge

Questions	Answers
1 Is a mandolin a stringed instrument or a keyboard instrument?	*Stringed*
2 In 1993 who became the 42nd President of the United States?	*Bill Clinton*
3 In Blackpool what is the Pepsi Max Big One?	*Roller coaster*
4 On which continent is the novel *Tarzan of the Apes* set?	*Africa*
5 Which former British Prime Minister was nicknamed The Iron Lady?	*Margaret Thatcher*
6 Which literary detective is associated with the phrase, "Elementary my dear Watson"?	*Sherlock Holmes*
7 Charlie Caroli, Coco and Grock are all the names of famous what?	*Clowns*
8 What type of bear is Soo, the friend of Sooty and Sweep?	*Panda*
9 What four-letter T word is the name given to a ballet dancer's skirt?	*Tutu*
10 What is found at the end of Noddy's hat?	*A bell*

Quiz 10
Question 4

Quiz 10
Question 8

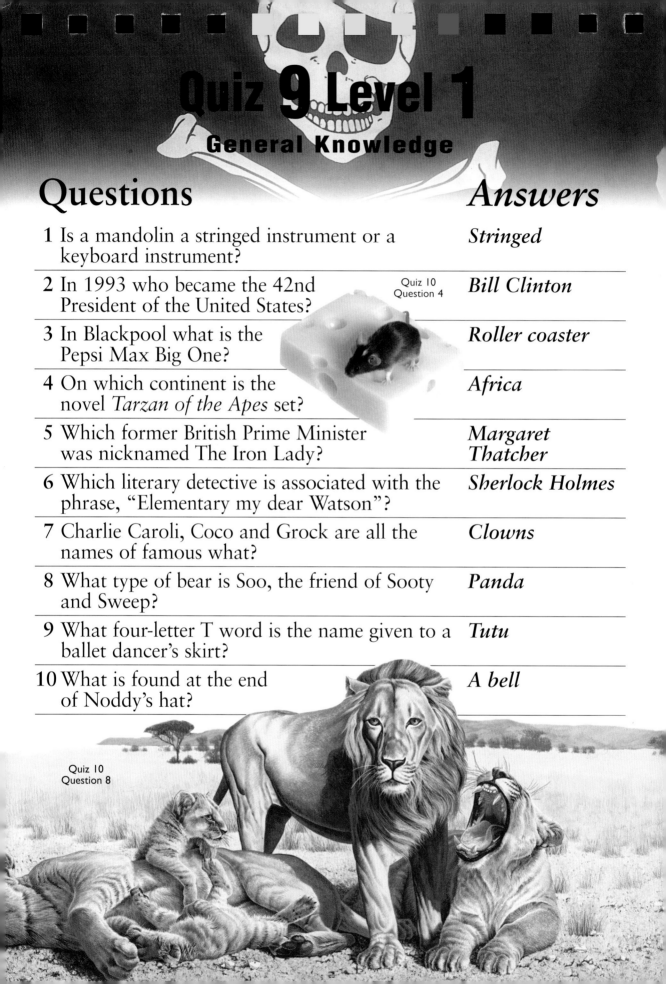

Quiz 10 Level 1
General Knowledge

Questions	Answers
1 Which sign of the zodiac is represented by an object as opposed to a person or an animal?	*Libra (scales)*
2 What country shares its name with a bird traditionally eaten at Christmas?	*Turkey*
3 What is the name given to the tombs of the pharaohs in ancient Egypt?	*Pyramids*
4 Which rodent do you associate with a computer?	*Mouse*
5 Traditionally, how many lives is a cat said to have?	*Nine*
6 In sea-going terms, what is the opposite of port?	*Starboard*
7 What does a bird have two of: stomachs or hearts?	*Stomachs*
8 Aslan, Clarence, Simba and Scar are all fictional names of what?	*Lions*
9 How many separate bones appear on a Jolly Roger flag?	*Three*
10 What day precedes Ash Wednesday?	*Shrove Tuesday*

Quiz 9
Question 9

Quiz 9
Question 1

Quiz 9
Question 7

Quiz 11 Level 1
Science and Maths

Questions	Answers
1 Maglev is short for what?	*Magnetic levitation*
2 How many grams are in 5 kilograms?	*5,000 (5 x 1,000)*
3 Which gas has the chemical symbol O?	*Oxygen*
4 To what does the adjective lunar apply?	*The Moon*
5 How many inches are there in four feet?	*48 (4 x 12)*
6 What remains if a dozen is subtracted from a baker's dozen?	*One (13-12)*
7 In physics, is a capital E the symbol for evaporation or energy?	*Energy*
8 Sheet and fork are both types of what weather phenomena?	*Lightning*
9 What A word is the substance produced when a person is angry, excited or frightened?	*Adrenalin*
10 Which has the most sides, a pentagon, an octagon or a hexagon?	*Octagon (eight sides)*

Quiz 12
Question 10

Quiz 12
Question 5

Questions

1 What is one quarter of 1,000?

2 What is larger: 50% or $^5/_8$?

3 How many degrees are there in a right angle?

Quiz 11
Question 4

4 Which part of the body contains the cornea, the retina and the pupil?

5 Indigo is sandwiched by blue and violet in what kind of naturally occurring phenomena?

6 If a number is multiplied, does it increase or decrease in size?

7 Frenchman Andre Ampere gave his name to a unit of what?

8 In total, how many sides would three rectangles and three triangles have?

9 What metal with the symbol Hg is used in thermometers?

10 Which Roman God gave his name to the largest planet in our solar system?

Answers

250

$^5/_8$

90

The eye

A rainbow

Increase in size

Electrical current (Amp)

21(12+9)

Mercury

Jupiter

Quiz 11
Question 8

Questions

		Answers
1	Is the letter S the chemical symbol for silver or sulphur?	*Sulphur*
2	The pen is the female, the cob the male and the cygnet the young. What is the bird?	*A swan*
3	What word can follow elder, goose, black, straw and rasp?	*Berry*
4	What part of an elephant is also the name for a large box in which clothes are kept?	*Trunk*
5	Ping-pong is another name for which popular game?	*Table Tennis*
6	What anniversary is celebrated for 50 years of marriage?	*Golden*
7	What number connects blind mice, musketeers and wise men?	*Three*
8	In the Bible what is referred to as the staff of life?	*Bread*
9	What three-letter word is the name given to an item sold at an auction?	*Lot*
10	What is the nationality of the pop group Westlife?	*Irish*

Quiz 14
Question 10

Quiz 14
Question 4

Questions	Answers
1 The name of what spice is also a slang term for red hair?	*Ginger*
2 In which garden did God put Adam and Eve?	*Garden of Eden*
3 Who changed the name of his flagship from the *Pelican* to the *Golden Hind*?	*Sir Francis Drake*
4 Geronimo and Sitting Bull are both the names of famous what?	*Native American Indians*
5 Through which continent does the River Nile flow?	*Africa*
6 What household item is also the name for the tail of a fox?	*Brush*
7 What word can follow beach, base, soft and foot?	*Ball*
8 How many stars are there on the United States flag?	*50*
9 Which American author wrote the classic novel *The Scarlet Letter*?	*Nathaniel Hawthorne*
10 Is the cross on the Swiss flag red, white or blue?	*White*

Quiz 13
Question 3

Quiz 13
Question 2

Quiz 15 Level 1
Geography

Questions	Answers
1 Is Philadelphia north-east or south-west of New York?	*South-west*
2 Stockholm is the capital of which country?	*Sweden*
3 Danish people are citizens of which country?	*Denmark*
4 On which continent does Luxembourg lie?	*Europe*
5 What is the world famous bridge in San Francisco called?	*Golden Gate Bridge*
6 What D word is the name given to the language spoken by people from Holland?	*Dutch*
7 Which English island county lies south of Hampshire?	*Isle of Wight*
8 Is California on the west coast or east coast of the United States?	*West coast*
9 The design of Blackpool Tower is based on which French building?	*Eiffel Tower*
10 The name of which major American city is sometimes shortened to L.A.?	*Los Angeles*

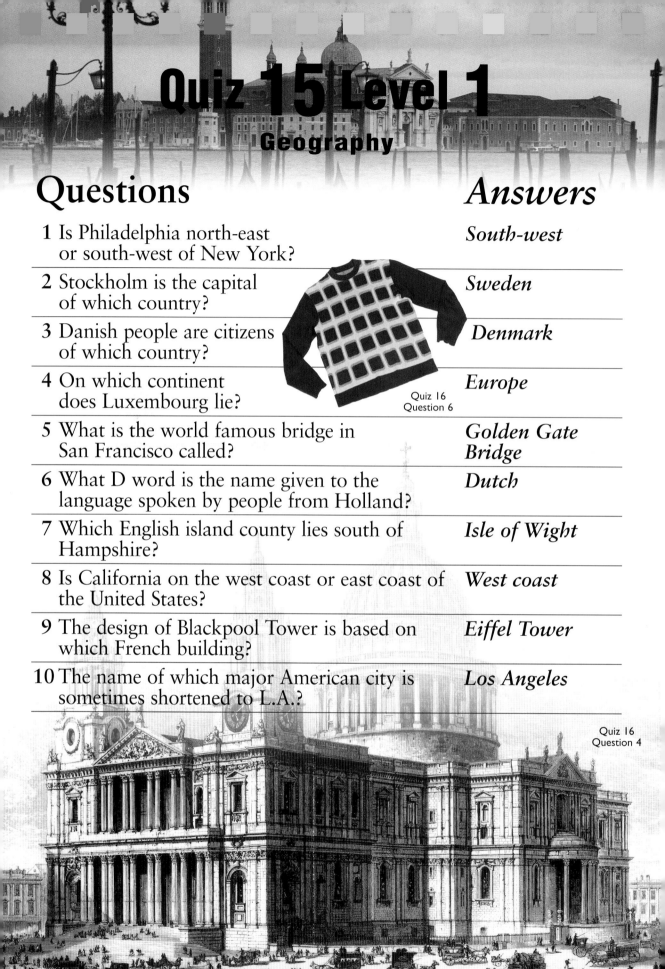

Quiz 16
Question 6

Quiz 16
Question 4

Quiz 16 Level 1
Geography

Questions	Answers
1 Which city in Scotland has the highest population?	*Glasgow*
2 In which country might you eat paella, drink sangria and hear flamenco music in Granada?	*Spain*
3 Which river runs alongside the Luxor Temple in Egypt?	*The Nile*
4 Which London building boasts a dome that stands 366 ft (111.56 m) above the pavement?	*St. Paul's Cathedral*
5 Melbourne is the capital of which Australian state?	*Victoria*
6 Which member of the Channel Islands is also the name of an article of clothing?	*Jersey*
7 What is the furthest south, South Africa, South America or the South Pole?	*South Pole*
8 On a map of Europe which country is shaped like a boot?	*Italy*
9 Which currency was adopted by 12 E.U. countries on January 1, 2002?	*The Euro*
10 What is the largest country in South America?	*Brazil*

Quiz 15 Question 3

Quiz 15 Question 5

Questions	Answers
1 What flower is the symbol of the British Labour Party?	*Red rose*
2 Granny Smith and Golden Delicious are both varieties of which fruit?	*Apple*
3 What instrument has 88 black and white keys?	*Piano*
4 What part of Peter Pan was kept in a drawer?	*His shadow*
5 What is your scapula?	*Shoulder blade*
6 From what animal is mutton obtained?	*Sheep*
7 In a pack of playing cards, how many clubs are there?	*13*
8 What are Ainsley Harriot and Jamie Oliver famous for?	*They are both chefs*
9 If you scored 15 out of 20 in a maths test what percentage of questions would be right?	*75%*
10 How many players in an ice hockey team are allowed on the ice during play?	*Six*

Quiz 18
Question 3

Quiz 18
Question 8

Questions	Answers
1 Brazil, cashew and pecan are all types of what?	*Nuts*
2 In which of the armed forces did Prince Andrew serve?	*Royal Navy*
3 Burmese and Persian are both breeds of which common household pet?	*Cat*
4 In mythology, how many eyes did the Cyclops have?	*One*
5 What is the third planet from the Sun?	*Earth*
6 In which African country is Tripoli?	*Libya*
7 *Costa* is the Spanish word for what?	*Coast*
8 What is manufactured in a mint: is it coins, knives or toffee?	*Coins*
9 Premiership football stars Thierry Henry and Fabian Barthez, both share which nationality?	*French*
10 How many balls are on a snooker table at the start of a match?	*22*

Quiz 17
Question 2

Quiz 17
Question 3

Quiz 19 Level 1

English

Questions	Answers
1 Which day of the week is also the name of Robinson Crusoe's manservant?	*Friday*
2 I visited the city of London yesterday. What is the proper noun in that sentence?	*London*
3 If a person is described as thrifty: are they generous or careful with money?	*Careful with money*
4 What word can precede pole, ship and stone?	*Flag*
5 What three-letter word can be a writing implement and an enclosure for animals?	*Pen*
6 How many books make up a trilogy?	*Three*
7 What animals does the adjective equine refer to?	*Horses*
8 In *The Lord of the Rings* is Gandalf a witch, a wizard or a hobbit?	*Wizard*
9 What is the name given to a young elephant, a young cow and a young whale?	*Calf*
10 What is the last vowel in the English alphabet?	*U*

Quiz 20
Question 6

Quiz 20
Question 8

Questions

Answers

1 Is the word fish a noun, a verb, or both? — *Both*

2 Fill in the blank, according to the saying "Every ……. has its day". — *Dog*

3 The cunning fox escaped from the hounds by hiding up a tree. What word is the adjective? — *Cunning (descriptive word)*

4 How many vowels does the word vowels have? — *Two (o and e)*

5 What is the past tense of the word shoot? — *Shot*

6 What three-letter word can precede ring, stone and hole? — *Key*

7 Which Shakespeare play is commonly referred to as the Scottish play? — Macbeth

8 In the Roald Dahl story, what giant fruit did James sail in? — *Peach*

9 What four-letter F word is given to a large pointed tooth? — *Fang*

10 What is the crime of intentionally setting fire to property known as? — *Arson*

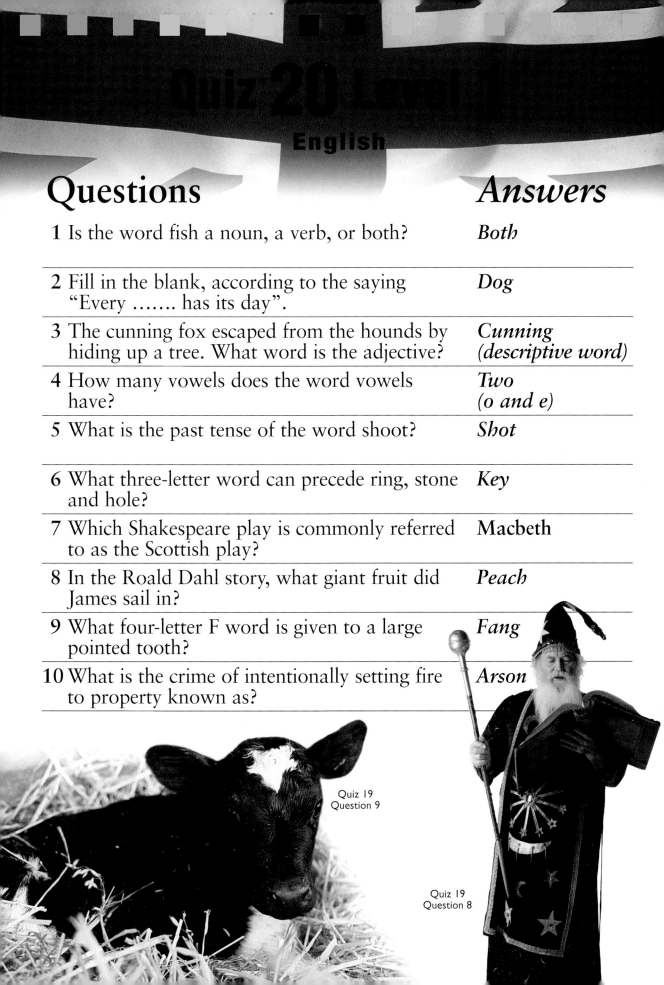

Quiz 19
Question 9

Quiz 19
Question 8

Quiz 21 Level 1
General Knowledge

Questions	Answers
1 Which of Inspector Morse's cars shares its name with a wild cat?	*Jaguar*
2 Which cartoon character was often referred to by the initials T.C.?	*Top Cat*
3 What is the lightest metal?	*Lithium*
4 What type of violent wind measures 12 on the Beaufort Scale?	*Hurricane*
5 Which sitcom character is associated with the catchphrase "I don't believe it"?	*Victor Meldrew*
6 Where were the words "Houston, Tranquility base here. The Eagle has landed" spoken from?	*The Moon*
7 Who lived in 100 Acre Wood, was it Rupert the Bear, Pooh Bear or Yogi Bear?	*Pooh Bear*
8 Which of the four seasons do Americans call the fall?	*Autumn*
9 Which country did minestrone soup originate from?	*Italy*
10 In Greek mythology what was Pegasus?	*A winged horse*

Quiz 22
Question 9

Quiz 22
Question 8

Questions	Answers
1 Who was the first child of Queen Elizabeth II to be married?	*Princess Anne (1973)*
2 What title is given to the wife of the American President?	*First Lady*
3 Who is Steve Cauthen?	*U.S. jockey*
4 What is the largest mammal that ever lived?	*Blue Whale*
5 Digestive, Garibaldi and Bourbon are types of what?	*Biscuit*
6 The prefix quin refers to which number?	*Five*
7 Four types of weather can be described as precipitation. Snow, rain, sleet and which other?	*Hail*
8 In which building in England are the Crown Jewels on display?	*Tower of London*
9 What type of crustacean is the symbol for the star sign Cancer?	*Crab*
10 What type of eagle is the national symbol of the United States?	*Bald eagle*

Quiz 21
Question 6

Quiz 21
Question 1

Quiz 23 Level 1
T.V. and Film

Questions	Answers
1 In which bay is the Australian soap *Home and Away* set?	*Summer Bay*
2 Which young wizard is played on film by Daniel Radcliffe?	*Harry Potter*
3 Which T.V. soap is set in the district of Walford?	Eastenders
4 Which actor appeared in *Seven*, *Snatch* and *Ocean's Eleven*?	*Brad Pitt*
5 Who is the cowboy character from *Toy Story*?	*Woody*
6 Which king of rock and roll starred in the films *Jailhouse Rock* and *Blue Hawaii*?	*Elvis Presley*
7 What type of cat is the villain of the piece in the Disney film *The Jungle Book*?	*Tiger*
8 Who played a Charlie's Angel and Mary in *There's Something About Mary*?	*Cameron Diaz*
9 Name the actor who played the character of Neo in the film *The Matrix*.	*Keanu Reeves*
10 What is the stage name of Doris von Kappelhof?	*Doris Day*

Quiz 24
Question 7

Quiz 24
Question 10

Questions

Answers

1 Which Italian city is also the name of a female character from *The Magic Roundabout*? — *Florence*

2 Which brick road did the characters follow in *The Wizard of Oz*? — *The Yellow Brick Road*

3 Where does Bart Simpson live? — *Springfield*

4 In 1986, which U.S. actor became mayor of Carmel, California? — *Clint Eastwood*

5 Who played Indiana Jones in three films in the 20th century? — *Harrison Ford*

6 Which cartoon duck was 65 years old in 1999? — *Donald Duck*

Quiz 23
Question 6

7 What mode of transport is central to the plot in the film *Top Gun*? — *Aeroplanes (jet fighters)*

8 In which film did Tom Hanks find himself alone on a remote desert island? — **Cast Away**

9 Which evil character is played by Anthony Hopkins in the film *The Silence of the Lambs*? — *Hannibal Lecter*

10 In 2000 Leonardo DiCaprio and Robert Carlyle starred in which film? — **The Beach**

Quiz 23
Question 7

Questions	Answers
1 In Greek mythology, who was the huge monster with nine heads?	*Hydra*
2 How many tarsal bones are there in a human's foot?	*Seven*
3 In the fairy story *Jack and the Beanstalk* what animal did Jack exchange for a few beans?	*A cow*
4 Peter Parker is the secret identity of which super hero?	*Spiderman*
5 Pharoahs were ancient rulers in which country?	*Egypt*
6 In the French language is *le soir*, the morning or the evening?	*The evening*
7 What letter is used for the international registration code on cars from Germany?	*D*
8 What is the adopted name of U.S. boxer Cassius Clay?	*Mohammed Ali*
9 What fruits are dried to make prunes?	*Plums*
10 What is an integer?	*Any whole number*

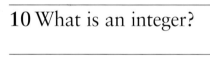

Quiz 26
Question 5

Quiz 26
Question 9

Quiz 26 Level 1
General Knowledge

Questions	Answers
1 Where did the sauce used in the dish spaghetti bolognese originate?	*Bologna*
2 What chocolate bar is advertised with the slogan "Lets you work, rest and play"?	*Mars bar*
3 What kind of food is gazpacho?	*Soup*
4 Acorns are the fruit of which tree?	*Oak*
5 During World War II, what were U Boats?	*Submarines*
6 In computer terminology what does R.A.M. stand for?	*Random Access Memory*
7 What vegetable does Bugs Bunny like best of all?	*Carrots*
8 What surname does Samuel, the code inventor and a police inspector called Endeavour, share?	*Morse*
9 In which sport do players throw projectiles from the oche?	*Darts*
10 Who did Cain kill in the first book of the Bible?	*Abel*

Quiz 25
Question 3

Quiz 25
Question 9

Quiz 27 Level 1
Sport

Questions	Answers
1 Which of the following sports does not involve using a horse: harness racing, shinty or polo?	*Shinty*
2 What did Tessa Sanderson win in 1984 and Linford Christie in 1992?	*An Olympic gold medal*
3 What is worn in the mouth by boxers to protect their teeth?	*A gum shield*
4 Which combat sport uses a bamboo stick called a shinai?	*Kendo*
5 What letter of the alphabet do rugby goal posts form?	*H*
6 Which football ground is known as the Theatre of Dreams?	*Old Trafford*
7 Which watersport was originally called soccer-in-water?	*Water Polo*
8 What animal print is on the shorts worn by boxer Prince Naseem?	*Leopard's spots*
9 Which race is run over a distance of 42,129 km / 26 mi 385 yds?	*The Marathon*
10 Who is the younger, Serena Williams or Venus Williams?	*Serena Williams*

Quiz 28
Question 8

Quiz 28
Question 2

Sport

Questions	Answers
1 In boxing, what does T.K.O. stand for?	*Technical knockout*
2 Which sport features in the 2002 film *The Mean Machine* starring Vinnie Jones?	*Football*
3 Which English city made a successful bid to host the 2002 Commonwealth Games?	*Manchester*
4 In which sport might you perform a triple salchow?	*Figure skating*
5 Who is the only member of a fielding cricket side allowed to wear gloves?	*Wicket keeper*
6 How many shots would a golfer have taken if scoring a birdie on a par 4 hole?	*Three shots*
7 How many players are in a basketball team?	*Five*
8 In which sport do the New York Yankees attempt to win the World Series?	*Baseball*
9 In which Scottish city do Hearts and Hibs play their home matches?	*Edinburgh*
10 Which jockey achieved the Magnificent Seven at Ascot in September 1996?	*Frankie Dettori*

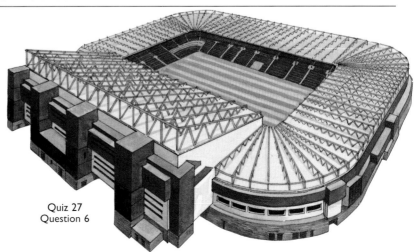

Quiz 27
Question 2

Quiz 27
Question 6

Quiz 29 Level 1
General Knowledge

Questions	Answers
1 What farmyard bird do you associate with the more common name of the disease *varicella*?	*Chicken (chickenpox)*
2 What grew in length when the puppet boy Pinnochio told lies?	*His nose*
3 According to the well known proverb, what begins at home?	*Charity*
4 What is the more common name of the capsicum?	*Red pepper*
5 Which shark is named after the shape of its head and a D.I.Y. tool?	*Hammerhead shark*
6 In the nursery rhyme, which bells said "You owe me five farthings"?	*The bells of St. Martins*
7 What is added to vodka to make a Bloody Mary?	*Tomato juice*
8 Who was the shorter of the Two Ronnies?	*Ronnie Corbett*
9 Who was the first woman mentioned in the Bible?	*Eve*
10 What is a basilisk?	*A lizard*

Quiz 30
Question 8

Quiz 30
Question 3

Questions	Answers
1 Name the biblical father of Shem, Ham and Japeth who built a vessel from gopher wood.	*Noah*
2 On which Mediterranean island was Napoleon Bonaparte born?	*Corsica*
3 Which saint's day is celebrated in Ireland on March 17?	*St. Patrick*
4 On a road what is a sleeping policeman?	*A traffic calming measure*
5 What word can precede sick, weed and side?	*Sea*
6 Which N word is the name of the addictive substance found in tobacco?	*Nicotine*
7 Which popular mint is also the name of a type of Volkswagon car?	*Polo*
8 What type of creature is Beatrix Potter's character Jeremy Fisher?	*Frog*
9 What was the Grimm Brothers' alternative name for Snow White?	*Snow Drop*
10 Who left Krypton, lived in Smallville, then gained employment in Metropolis?	*Superman*

Quiz 29
Question 5

Quiz 29
Question 4

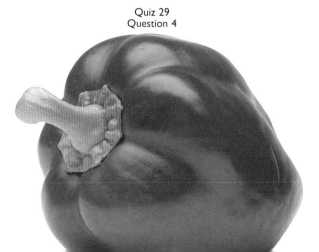

Quiz 31 Level 1
Natural World

Questions	Answers
1 Grass, adder and smooth are the only three species native to Great Britain: what are they?	*Snakes*
2 What kind of dam-building creature lives in a lodge?	*Beaver*
3 In the fish world: what are dorsals, tail and anal?	*They are all types of fin*
4 Is a worm a vertebrate or an invertebrate?	*Invertebrate (no backbone)*
5 What A word is the name given to the horns of a deer?	*Antlers*
6 Which reptile's name is sometimes shortened to gator?	*Alligator*
7 What occupation is also the name of a female goat?	*Nanny*
8 What mammal, native to Alaska, has a body covered with hair and barbed quills?	*Porcupine*
9 What four-letter word can follow blue, black, love and butcher?	*Bird*
10 Which comic strip beagle is the pet dog of Charlie Brown?	*Snoopy*

Quiz 32
Question 8

Quiz 32
Question 1

Quiz 32 Level 1

History

Questions	Answers
1 What happened in September 1666, after Thomas Farrimor forgot to turn off his oven?	*The Great Fire of London*
2 In which ocean did the *Titanic* sink?	*Atlantic Ocean*
3 In which century did General George Custer make his last stand?	*19th century*
4 Of the six wives of Henry VIII, how many had four letters in their first name?	*Three (two Annes and one Jane)*
5 Was Bill Clinton a Democrat or a Republican?	*Democrat*
6 Which prince did Flora Macdonald assist in escaping from Scotland?	*Bonnie Prince Charlie*
7 Who was nicknamed The Iron Duke and gave his name to an item of footwear?	*Duke of Wellington*
8 Which 18th century explorer sailed to Australia in the *Endeavour*?	*Captain James Cook*
9 In which war were tanks first used on the battlefield?	*First World War*
10 In which film did Mel Gibson play Scottish hero William Wallace?	**Braveheart**

Quiz 31
Question 2

Quiz 31
Question 8

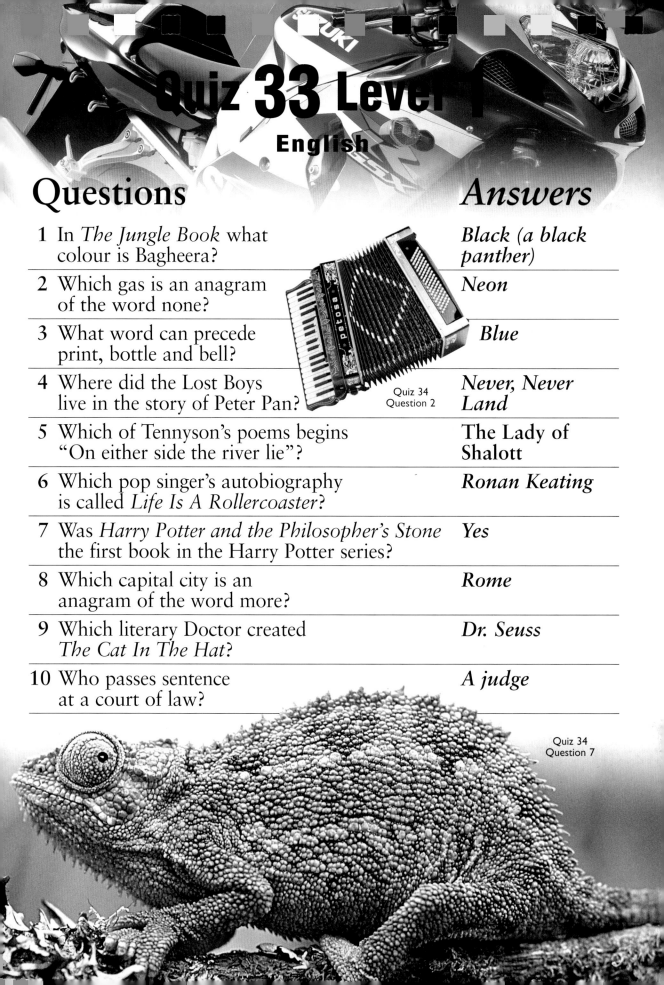

Questions

1 In *The Jungle Book* what colour is Bagheera?

2 Which gas is an anagram of the word none?

3 What word can precede print, bottle and bell?

4 Where did the Lost Boys live in the story of Peter Pan?

5 Which of Tennyson's poems begins "On either side the river lie"?

6 Which pop singer's autobiography is called *Life Is A Rollercoaster*?

7 Was *Harry Potter and the Philosopher's Stone* the first book in the Harry Potter series?

8 Which capital city is an anagram of the word more?

9 Which literary Doctor created *The Cat In The Hat*?

10 Who passes sentence at a court of law?

Answers

Black (a black panther)

Neon

Blue

Never, Never Land

The Lady of Shalott

Ronan Keating

Yes

Rome

Dr. Seuss

A judge

Quiz 34
Question 2

Quiz 34
Question 7

Quiz 34 Level 1
Music

Questions	Answers
1 What was the early name for the pianoforte?	*Fortepiano*
2 What instrument is often called a squeeze box?	*The accordion*
3 What was the title of the Spice Girls first U.K. No. 1 hit?	*"Wannabe"*
4 What is the last name of the singing sisters Dannii and Kylie?	*Minogue*
5 Which singer and actress sometimes abbreviates her name to J-Lo?	*Jennifer Lopez*
6 In the video for the Robbie Williams hit "Angels", does he ride a horse or motorbike?	*Motorbike*
7 In his hit record, what did Boy George sing after repeating the word karma five times?	*Chameleon*
8 What animated film about a green ogre climaxes with a karaoke session?	Shrek
9 What is the first name of John Travolta's character in *Grease*?	*Danny*
10 Are cymbals a percussion or brass instrument?	*Percussion*

Quiz 33
Question 5

Quiz 33
Question 2

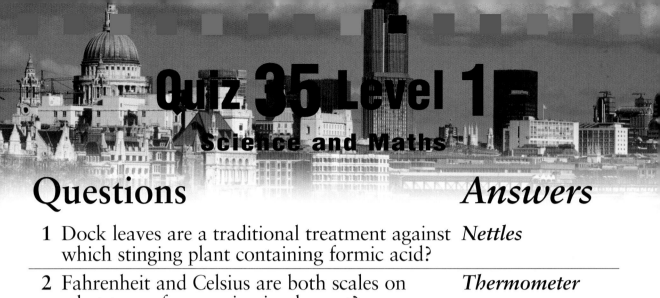

Quiz 35 Level 1
Science and Maths

Questions	Answers
1 Dock leaves are a traditional treatment against which stinging plant containing formic acid?	*Nettles*
2 Fahrenheit and Celsius are both scales on what type of measuring implement?	*Thermometer*
3 What comes between red and yellow in a rainbow?	*Orange*
4 On a magnet would a north pole attract or repel a south pole?	*Attract*
5 What is 10% of 1,000?	*100*
6 What is 27.5 doubled?	*55*
7 How many zeros are in a million?	*Six*
8 What did Carlton Magee invent in 1935?	*The parking meter*
9 How many angles in an isosceles triangle are equal?	*Two*
10 What is larger: 5 squared or 3 cubed?	*3 cubed (3x3x3= 27)*

Quiz 36
Question 9

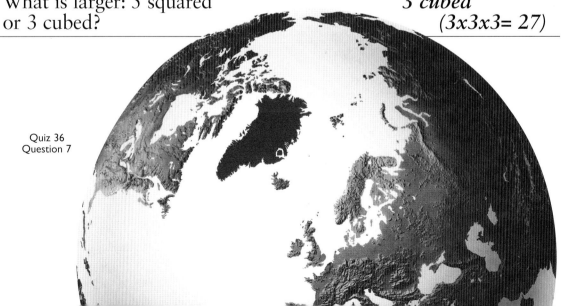

Quiz 36
Question 7

Quiz 36 Level 1
Geography

Questions	Answers
1 What is the alternative name for the Netherlands?	*Holland*
2 Which American state shares its name with a pop group?	*Texas*
3 In which city is the novel *Oliver Twist* set?	*London*
4 From which British city do Geordies hail?	*Newcastle*
5 What does the D stand for in Washington D.C.?	*District (of Colombia)*
6 In which country is Great Britain's highest mountain?	*Scotland (Ben Nevis)*
7 Which is the world's largest island?	*Greenland*
8 In which country are the cities Seville and Madrid?	*Spain*
9 Which gemstone provides part of the nickname of Ireland?	*Emerald (The Emerald Isle)*
10 In which Italian city did the Shakesperean merchant Antonio ply his trade?	*Venice*

Quiz 35
Question 1

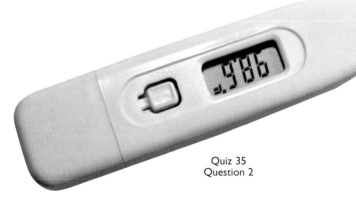

Quiz 35
Question 2

Quiz 37 Level 1
T.V. and Film

Questions	Answers
1 Which sport was featured in films *The Natural* and *A League of Their Own*?	Baseball
2 What was the title of the 1990 sequel to *Three Men and a Baby*?	Three Men and a Little Lady
3 Who has spent many years on T.V. battling against the Daleks?	Dr. Who
4 What is the name of Postman Pat's wife?	Sarah
5 What is the name of Mickey Mouse's pet dog?	Pluto
6 In the *Bugs Bunny* cartoons, is Yosemite Sam's beard black, red or white?	Red
7 What type of creature is Willy in the *Free Willy* films?	Killer whale
8 Which edible onions are also the name of the central family in the *Rugrats*?	Pickles
9 Who played Cruella de Vil in the 1996 film *101 Dalmations*?	Glenn Close
10 Which popular American chat show host, starred in the 1988 film *Hairspray*?	Ricki Lake

Quiz 38
Question 2

Quiz 38
Question 9

Quiz 38 Level 1
Sport

Questions	Answers
1 In which sport do England and Australia compete to win The Ashes?	*Cricket*
2 Ralf and Michael Schumacher are famous names in which sport?	*Motor racing*
3 What is the name of the only Scottish football league team beginning with K?	*Kilmarnock*
4 What are halyards used for?	*Hoisting sails*
5 How many minutes long is a round in boxing?	*Three minutes*
6 On a chessboard what piece is also a member of the clergy?	*Bishop*
7 How many cox in total compete in the Oxford and Cambridge boat race? Quiz 37 Question 7	*Two*
8 What fruit is traditionally eaten with cream at the Wimbledon tennis championships?	*Strawberries*
9 In which of the following sports is a volley not allowed: tennis, table tennis or badminton?	*Table tennis*
10 For which sport did Great Britain win a gold medal in the 2002 Winter Olympics?	*Curling*

Quiz 37
Question 1

Quiz 39 Level 1
General Knowledge

Questions	Answers
1 Eddie Murphy did the voice-over for which animal in the film *Shrek*?	*Donkey*
2 In which board game do players attempt to solve a murder at Tudor House?	*Cluedo*
3 Complete this well-known company's name Eastern Seaboard Standard...	*Oil (ESSO)*
4 What part of the body is a cardiologist concerned with?	*The heart*
5 What is the least powerful piece on a chessboard?	*Pawn*
6 What is colder the South Pole or the North Pole?	*South Pole*
7 Which country did Charles Rennie Mackintosh come from?	*Scotland*
8 What is combined with copper to make brass?	*Tin*
9 What is the name of the central female character in *Gone With The Wind*?	*Scarlett O'Hara*
10 What are a clove hitch and a reef?	*Types of knot*

Quiz 40
Question 2

Quiz 40
Question 8

Quiz 40 Level 1
General Knowledge

Questions	Answers
1 What three-word motto is used by the S.A.S.?	*Who Dares Wins*
2 What kind of flowers do we associate with Impressionist painter Claude Monet?	*Water lilies*
3 Closely associated with Count Dracula, in which country is the area of Transylvania?	*Romania*
4 What is sometimes referred to as Adam's ale?	*Water*
5 Ciabatta, pitta, soda and naan are all types of what?	*Bread*
6 Was *Indiana Jones and the Temple of Doom* the first or second film in the series?	*Second*
7 What is the name of the cotton costume worn by judo competitors?	*Judogi*
8 Which little bird is affectionately known as Jenny?	*The wren*
9 The Caspian Sea is the world's largest what?	*Lake*
10 What are kept in an apiary?	*Bees*

Quiz 39
Question 3

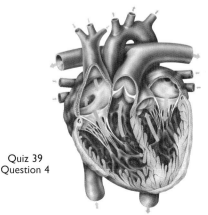

Quiz 39
Question 4

Quiz 41 Level 1

Natural World

Questions

		Answers
1	What animal is a cross between a mare and an ass?	*Mule*
2	Does a female walrus have tusks?	*Yes*
3	What is the plural of fungus?	*Fungi*
4	What name is given to a male horse or pony that is less than four years of age?	*Colt*
5	Is the stamen the male or female organ of a plant?	*Male organ*
6	What is the fatherly alternative name for a crane fly?	*Daddy-longlegs*
7	Is a young seal called a kitten, a pup or a cub?	*Pup*
8	What is the only bird that possesses nostrils?	*Kiwi*
9	Do snakes have eyelids?	*No*
10	From which flowers do we obtain opium?	*Poppies*

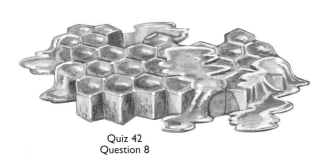

Quiz 42
Question 8

Quiz 42
Question 10

Quiz 42 Level 1
Natural World

Questions	Answers
1 Which bird native to the island of Mauritius became extinct in 1681?	*Dodo*
2 A Painted Lady, Red Admiral and Monarch are all species of what?	*Butterfly*
3 From which animal is the meat venison obtained?	*Deer*
4 What B word is the name given to whale fat?	*Blubber*
5 How many stomachs does a cow have?	*Four*
6 What is the world's tallest bird?	*Ostrich*
7 What is stored in a camel's hump?	*Fat*
8 What shape are honeycomb cells in a beehive?	*Hexagonal*
9 What kind of leaves provide the staple diet of a silkworm?	*Mulberry*
10 A male pig and a male bear share the same name, what is it?	*Boar*

Quiz 41
Question 8

Quiz 41
Question 3

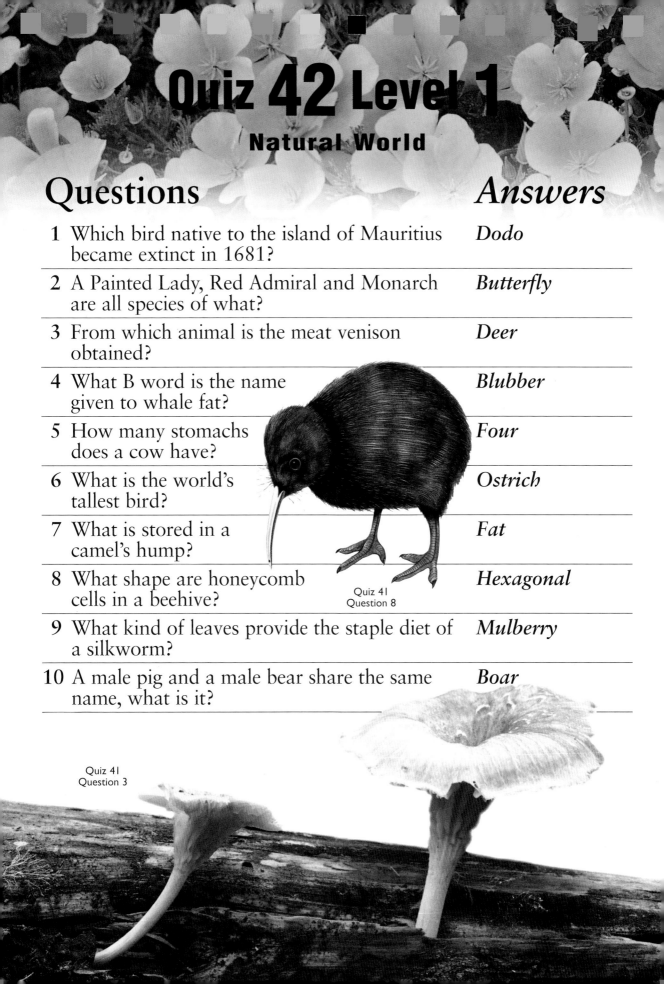

Quiz 43 Level 1
General Knowledge

Questions	Answers
1 Name the vehicle in which Donald Campbell died while attempting a water-speed record?	*Bluebird*
2 Who was the oldest of The Marx Brothers: Gummo, Groucho, Chico, Harpo or Zeppo?	*Chico*
3 According to the legend, when the apes leave so will the British. Which rock is referred to?	*Rock of Gibraltar*
4 Associated with the town of Assisi, who is the patron saint of animals?	*St. Francis*
5 What word can precede bump, boat, limit and trap?	*Speed*
6 Which headgear do we associate with comedian Tommy Cooper?	*A fez*
7 According to the nursery rhyme who killed Cock Robin?	*The sparrow*
8 What is a blacksmith's workshop called?	*Forge*
9 A.K. is the abbreviation for which American state?	*Alasaka*
10 On T.V. who is known as the Naked Chef?	*Jamie Oliver*

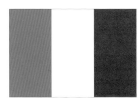

Quiz 44
Question 9

Quiz 44
Question 3

Quiz 44 Level 1
General Knowledge

Questions	Answers
1 What is the name of the baker in the card game *Happy Families*?	*Mr Bun*
2 Which literary bear shares his name with a railway station built by I.K. Brunel?	*Paddington*
3 Which Italian city is famed for its leaning tower?	*Pisa*
4 In which country was Pope John II born?	*Poland*
5 Stud, Indian and Draw are all types of which card game?	*Poker*
6 The Howrah in Calcutta and Rialto in Venice are both names of what?	*Bridges*
7 What is celebrated on the fourth Thursday in November every year in the United States?	*Thanksgiving Day*
8 Which of The Beatles was barefoot on the album cover for *Abbey Road*?	*Paul McCartney*
9 In which country was the gangster Al Capone born?	*Italy*
10 What three-letter first name for a boy is also a Spanish word for Mr.?	*Don*

Quiz 43
Question 6

Quiz 43
Question 1

Questions	Answers
1 George V, Edward VIII, George VI and Elizabeth II all belong to which royal house?	*House of Windsor*
2 Which continent was Ernest Shackleton famous for exploring?	*Antarctica*
3 Who defeated King Harold at the Battle of Hastings in 1066?	*William the Conqueror*
4 Name the first woman to fly in space?	*Valentina Tereshkova*
5 In 1909 who made the first flight across the English Channel?	*Louis Bleriot*
6 Catherine II of Russia is better known as what?	*Catherine the Great*
7 What is named after the German physicist Hans Geiger?	*The Geiger Counter*
8 In November 1605, which conspiracy to blow up James I and Parliament, was uncovered?	*The Gunpowder Plot*
9 Baron Manfred Von Richthofen or the Red Baron was a pilot during which war?	*World War I*
10 Which historical age preceded the Iron Age?	*The Bronze Age*

Quiz 46
Question 3

Quiz 46 Level 1

History

Questions	Answers
1 Which building gave its name to the scandal resulting in the downfall of Richard Nixon?	*Watergate Building*
2 Which king did Sean Connery portray in the film *Robin Hood, Prince of Thieves*?	*Richard the Lionheart*
3 Name the Italian dictator who was known as Il Duce?	*Benito Mussolini*
4 In which battle did Horatio Nelson die in 1805?	*The Battle of Trafalgar*
5 What destroyed the Japanese cities of Hiroshima and Nagasaki in August 1945?	*An atomic bomb*
6 Which Native American Indian tribe was led by Geronimo?	*Apache*
7 Who crossed the Alps with his army and 57 elephants?	*Hannibal*
8 Who resigned as Secretary of State for War in 1963, following an infamous scandal?	*John Profumo*
9 In 1912 what became the first ship to use the newly adapted S.O.S. distress signal?	**Titanic**
10 Davy Crockett's hat was made from the skin and fur of which animal?	*Racoon*

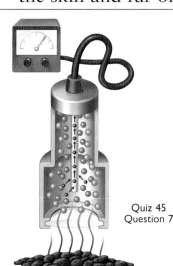

Quiz 45
Question 7

Quiz 45
Question 3

Quiz 47 Level 1

General Knowledge

Questions	Answers
1 What nickname is given to British Internet users over the age of 55?	*Silver Surfers*
2 What R word is the name given to a teacher of Jewish law?	*Rabbi*
3 In which English county is the village of Stilton?	*Cambridgeshire*
4 What turns litmus paper red?	*Acid*
5 Is a dulcimer a kitchen implement or a stringed instrument?	*A stringed instrument*
6 What C word is the name given to the framework on which a motorcar is mounted?	*Chassis*
7 What flying mammals use sonar echolocation to find their food?	*Bats*
8 Which children's characters did Father Abraham accompany in the 1970s?	*The Smurfs*
9 It is the world's first national park and features Old Faithful: what is it called?	*Yellowstone*
10 What flower shares its name with a part of the eyeball?	*Iris*

Quiz 48
Question 10

Quiz 48
Question 2

Quiz 48 Level 1
General Knowledge

Questions	Answers

Questions

Answers

1 Name the T.V. actor who led *The A Team*?

George Peppard

2 What kind of vehicle is a B.S.A. Golden Flash?

A motorbike

Quiz 47
Question 7

3 Which comedian created the character of Fred Scuttle?

Benny Hill

4 Helsinki is the capital of which Scandinavian country?

Finland

5 The capital of Hong Kong shares its name with a girl's first name: what is it?

Victoria

6 Which best selling writer, wrote the novels *Tilly Trotter* and *The Cinder Path*?

Catherine Cookson

7 What is the name of Donald Duck's girlfriend?

Daisy Duck

8 Which English river is spanned by 27 bridges and rises in the Cotswolds?

River Thames

9 What kind of bird is Captain Flint in *Treasure Island*?

Parrot

10 The drink perry is made from which fruit?

Pears

Quiz 47
Question 5

Quiz 49 Level 2
Science and Maths

Questions	Answers
1 What does molten lava flow out of?	*Volcanoes*
2 What is the only metal that is liquid at room temperature?	*Mercury*
3 What name is given to an angle of less than 90 degrees?	*Acute*
4 What is the cubed root of 64?	*Four (4x4x4=64)*
5 What chemical element has the symbol Ni?	*Nickel*
6 Where would you find 42 spots?	*On a pair of dice (21x 2)*
7 What is the lowest two-digit prime number?	*Eleven*
8 Where is the Sea of Showers?	*The Moon*
9 How many right angles are there in a rectangle?	*Four*
10 How many sides does a hexagon have?	*Six*

Quiz 50
Question 10

Quiz 50 Level 2
Science and Maths

Questions	Answers
1 What is the three-letter name of the space station launched by the U.S.S.R. in 1986?	*Mir*
2 How many feet are in a fathom?	*Six*
3 Is the letter C the chemical symbol for copper, cobalt or carbon?	*Carbon*
4 How many copies a year do you get of a quarterly magazine?	*Four*
5 What E word is the name given to the outer layer of the skin?	*Epidermis*
6 What A word is a form of mathematics in which letters are used in place of numbers?	*Algebra*
7 What is 70% of 200?	*140*
8 How many sides of equal length does a scalene triangle have?	*None*
9 Nucleus, coma and tail are the three main parts of a what?	*A comet*
10 What type of spacecraft was first launched in April 1981?	*Space shuttle*

Quiz 49
Question 6

Quiz 49
Question 1

Quiz 51 Level 2

General Knowledge

Questions	Answers
1 What two countries make up the Iberian Peninsula?	*Spain and Portugal*
2 Is a fir tree evergreen or deciduous?	*Evergreen*
3 In which city did Catherine Zeta Jones marry Michael Douglas?	*New York*
4 What are dabs and flounders?	*Flat fish*
5 In polite circles is the drink port passed to the right or the left?	*To the left*
6 In Greek mythology Eros was the god of what?	*Love*
7 In a court of law what name is given to the decision reached by a jury?	*Verdict*
8 In which film did Tom Hanks say "Houston, we have a problem"?	**Apollo 13**
9 What type of snake is said to have killed Cleopatra?	*An asp*
10 In what activity would a person wear self-contained underwater breathing apparatus?	*Scuba diving*

Quiz 52
Question 10

Quiz 52 Level 2
General Knowledge

Questions	Answers
1 What kind of animals are the cartoon characters Chip 'n Dale?	*Chipmunks*
2 What connects Anne Frank, Samuel Pepys and Adrian Mole?	*The all wrote diaries*
3 Which Welsh actor married Elizabeth Taylor on two occasions?	*Richard Burton*
4 What name connects a horse in *Toy Story 2* and a dog in *Oliver Twist*?	*Bullseye*
5 In Roman numerals what letter of the alphabet represents 500?	*D*
6 What car manufacturer makes the Golf and Beetle models?	*Volkswagon*
7 Which is the only dog breed to have a blue-black tongue?	*Chow Chow*
8 What did the American Samuel Colt invent in 1835?	*The revolver*
9 What hard substance forms the outermost layer of the human tooth?	*Enamel*
10 What kind of tournament was central to the plot of the 2001 film *A Knight's Tale*?	*Jousting tournament*

Quiz 51
Question 4

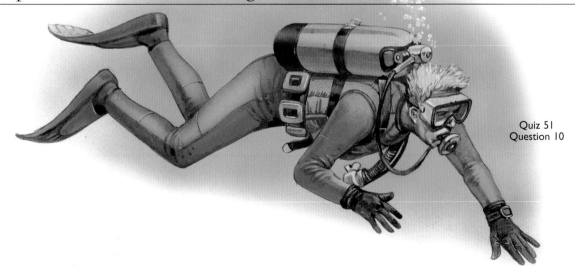

Quiz 51
Question 10

Quiz 53 Level 2
Geography

Questions	Answers
1 On which thoroughfare in London does the Cenotaph War Memorial stand?	*Whitehall*
2 What is the name of the New York avenue associated with the advertising industry?	*Madison Avenue*
3 Which capital city provided the title of a 1981 hit record for Ultravox?	*Vienna*
4 What is the only American state that begins with the letter P?	*Pennsylvania*
5 What is the national flower of Scotland?	*Thistle*
6 On which river does the city of New Orleans stand?	*Mississippi*
7 Which Scottish city gave its name to a type of cake?	*Dundee*
8 In France what mode of transport is the T.G.V.?	*High speed train*
9 Which Mediterranean island's flag includes an image of the George Cross?	*Malta*
10 On which Caribbean island is the resort of Montego Bay?	*Jamaica*

Quiz 54
Question 10

Quiz 54
Question 4

Questions	Answers
1 In which city was Terry Waite taken hostage in 1987?	*Beirut*
2 The French town of Dijon is famed for the manufacture of which condiment?	*Mustard*
3 The River Taff flows through which British capital city?	*Cardiff*
4 What is the nickname for the state of Kansas?	*Sunflower State*
5 In which European city is the headquarters of the Red Cross?	*Geneva*
6 Which country did the U.S.S.R. invade in 1979 and the U.S. invade in 2001?	*Afghanistan*
7 In which century did the British rule of India end?	*20th century*
8 What building in the seaside resort of Brighton was built for King George IV?	*Brighton Royal Pavilion*
9 Which American state is the nearest to Russia?	*Alaska*
10 Which famous statue in the U.S. was built on Bedloe's Island?	*Statue of Liberty*

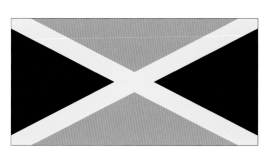

Quiz 53
Question 10

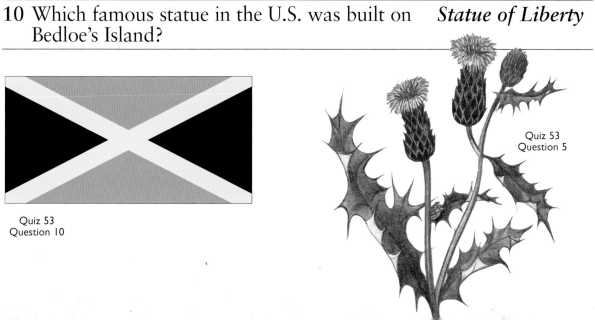

Quiz 53
Question 5

Questions	Answers
1 What animal represents the star sign that falls between July 24 and August 23?	*Lion (for Leo)*
2 Is a Tasmanian Devil a rodent, a marsupial or a reptile?	*A marsupial*
3 Which member of the British Royal family was born in August 1988?	*Princess Beatrice*
4 Which strong sailor man did Robin Williams play in a 1980 film?	*Popeye*
5 What number is represented by the phrase Kelly's eye in bingo slang?	*One*
6 What animal is the symbol for the World Wildlife Fund for Nature?	*Giant panda*
7 Flemish, German and Walloon are the official languages of which European country?	*Belgium*
8 In the film *Cleopatra*, what was the name of the Roman general played by Richard Burton?	*Marc Anthony*
9 Which river 1,500 km in length, flows through Calcutta and is considered sacred in India?	*Ganges*
10 Which fruit is traditionally eaten during Wimbledon fortnight?	*Strawberries*

Quiz 56
Question 3

Quiz 56
Question 2

Quiz 56 Level 2
General Knowledge

Questions	Answers
1 The pectorals are the main muscles in which part of the human body?	*The chest*
2 Trappist, Benedictine and Cistercians are all orders of what?	*Monks*
3 What is grown in a paddy field? *Quiz 55 Question 7*	*Rice*
4 What would you find growing in an arboretum?	*Trees*
5 In the Bible, whose wife was turned into a pillar of salt?	*The wife of Lot*
6 Which country's flag is nicknamed Old Glory?	*The United States*
7 What is known as the Red Planet?	*Mars*
8 Which English county's name literally means people of the north?	*Norfolk*
9 On children's T.V. what was the name of the duck that replaced Gordon the Gopher?	*Edd the Duck*
10 In Indian cooking what is a tandoor? *Quiz 55 Question 10*	*A clay oven*

Questions	Answers
1 Semaphore is a system of signalling using the arms or what else?	*Flags*
2 What do the initials C.B. in C.B. radio stand for?	*Citizen's Band*
3 Is an epilogue at the beginning or at the end of a book?	*At the end*
4 Choreography is the art of arranging what?	*Dance*
5 What do the initials I.C.U. stand for in a hospital?	*Intensive Care Unit*
6 What five-letter word can follow easy, electric and wheel?	*Chair*
7 Pimple and blotch is cockney rhyming slang for what? Quiz 58 Question 6	*Scotch (the drink)*
8 What A word is the name given to a drug that counteracts a poison?	*Antidote*
9 In the T.V. game show *Countdown*, how many letters does each contestant choose per round?	*Nine*
10 What does the letter P stand for in P.O.W.? Quiz 58 Question 9	*Prisoner (of War)*

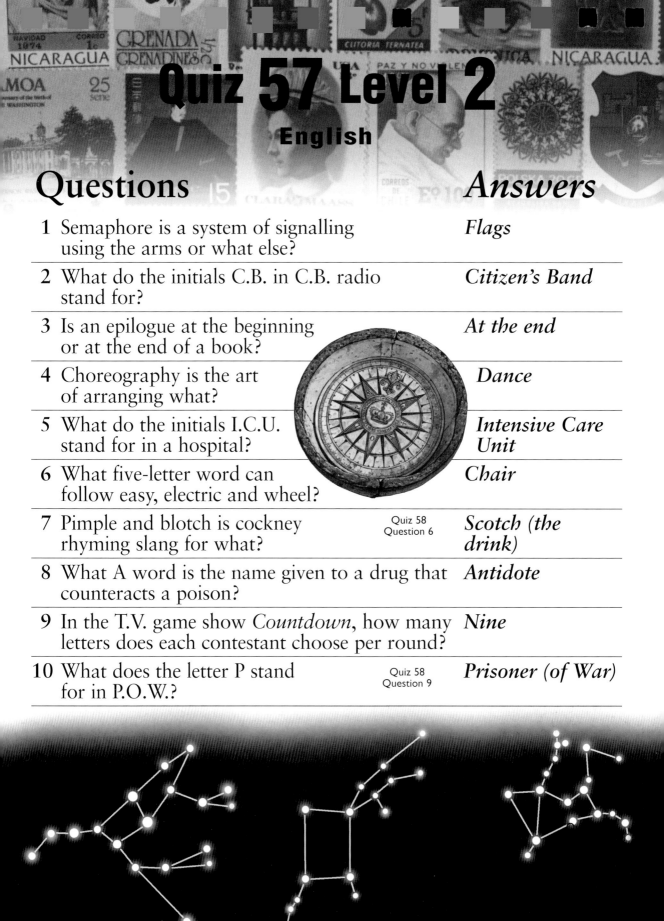

Quiz 58 Level 2

English

Questions	Answers
1 Is the spear side the male or female side of the family?	*Male side*
2 According to the proverb what sort of men tell no tales?	*Dead men*
3 According to the proverb, what makes the heart grow fonder?	*Absence*
4 What do the initials V.H.F. stand for?	*Very High Frequency*
5 What C word is the name given to an official in charge of a museum?	*Curator*
6 On a ship, which instrument used for showing direction, is housed in a binnacle?	*Compass*
7 What H word is the name given to the small stroke separating two words, as in re-enter?	*Hyphen*
8 The Penny Black was the first in the World. What was it?	*A postage stamp*
9 What C word is the name given to a collection of stars, e.g. Ursa Major and Ursa Minor?	*Constellations*
10 What is the shared name for a natural container for peas and a group of dolphins?	*Pod*

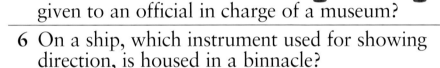

Quiz 57
Question 6

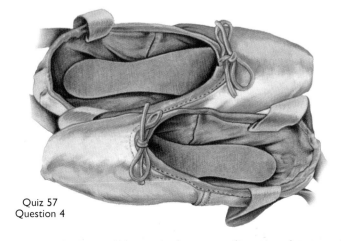

Quiz 57
Question 4

Quiz 59 Level 2
General Knowledge

Questions	Answers
1 In June 2001 who was named as the world's richest man for the 7th consecutive year?	*Bill Gates*
2 Shoguns were ancient military commanders from which country?	*Japan*
3 What is the name of the holiday camp in the sitcom *Hi-De-Hi*?	*Maplins*
4 What do you collect if you are a philatelist?	*Stamps*
5 Is Camembert a Swiss, French or German cheese?	*French*
6 In the fairytale *Cinderella* what was turned into a glass coach by the fairy godmother?	*Pumpkin*
7 What is the name of the R.A.F.'s aerobatic display team?	*Red Arrows*
8 In which Dutch city is the Vincent Van Gogh Museum?	*Amsterdam*
9 What star sign does a pair of fish represent?	*Pisces*
10 Is the sartorius muscle in the arm or the leg?	*The leg*

Quiz 60
Question 2

Quiz 60
Question 1

Questions	Answers
1 How many minutes are there in one day?	1,440
2 What type of stinging creatures lives in a vespiary?	Wasps
3 Name the body of water that lies directly south of Swansea Bay?	Bristol Channel
4 How many prongs are there on a tuning fork?	Two
5 Where did Wallace and Gromit go for a grand day out?	The Moon
6 Who did Vladimir Putin succeed as President of Russia?	Boris Yeltsin
7 Which island in the Irish Sea has an emblem that depicts a three-legged figure?	Isle of Man
8 In the children's T.V. series *Rainbow*, what type of animal is George?	A hippopotamus
9 On which Scottish river was the Queen Elizabeth liner built?	The River Clyde
10 Diana Prince is the secret identity of which superhero?	Wonder Woman

Quiz 59
Question 6

Quiz 59
Question 1

Quiz 61 Level 2

T.V. and Music

Questions	Answers
1 "Never Ever" was the first No. 1 for which girl band?	*All Saints*
2 In which city is the series *ER* set?	*Chicago*
3 Irish musician James Galway is particularly associated with which instrument?	*Flute*
4 Which opera house was opened in 1973 and looks like yachts in full sail?	*Sydney Opera House*
5 Who narrated the *Blue Planet* documentary series?	*David Attenborough*
6 Who plays Dana Scully in *The X Files*?	*Gillian Anderson*
7 In 1993, which chart topper sang "I'd Do Anything For Love, But I Won't Do That"?	*Meatloaf*
8 On which game show are Ally McCoist and John Parrott opposing team captains?	*A Question Of Sport*
9 What musical percussion instrument is named after its geometrical shape?	*Triangle*
10 Gordon Sumner and Stuart Copeland were members of which 80s band?	*The Police*

Quiz 62
Question 8

Quiz 62
Question 6

Quiz 62 Level 2

T.V. and Music

	Questions	Answers
1	Which comedian created the characters of Alan Partridge and Tony Ferrino?	*Steve Coogan*
2	Who early in his career appeared in *Neighbours*, before finding screen fame playing a gladiator?	*Russell Crowe*
3	Name the former lead singer of The Jam, who is nicknamed The Mod Father?	*Paul Weller*
4	At what time of the day is a serenade traditionally sung?	*The evening*
5	*Holby City* is a spin off from which medical drama?	*Casualty*
6	Burgess Meredith and Danny De Vito have both played which arch enemy of Batman?	*The Penguin*
7	Who had a hit with "It's Raining Men" in 2001 and entertained British troops in Oman?	*Geri Halliwell*
8	Courtesy of the 1990 World Cup finals, who enjoyed a hit single with "Nessun Dorma"?	*Luciano Pavarotti*
9	Who provided the voices of the animals in the 60s T.V. series *Animal Magic*?	*Johnny Morris*
10	In *The Flintstones*, who is the father of Bam Bam?	*Barney Rubble*

Quiz 61
Question 9

Quiz 61
Question 4

Quiz 63 Level 2
General Knowledge

Questions	Answers
1 Who was the brother of Mary and Martha raised from the dead by Jesus?	*Lazarus*
2 On which planet is Olympic Mons, the largest known volcano in the solar system?	*Mars*
3 Who rode a horse called Black Bess and was executed by hanging in the city of York?	*Dick Turpin*
4 What is the first name of Paul McCartney's fashion designer daughter?	*Stella*
5 In which decade did Alexander Fleming discover penicillin?	*1920s*
6 Which Cuban leader was code-named The Beard by the C.I.A.?	*Fidel Castro*
7 Which actress starred in the films *E.T.* and *Charlie's Angels*?	*Drew Barrymore*
8 What species of spider has varieties called Goliath and Cobalt Blue?	*Tarantula*
9 Which pace comes between a trot and a gallop?	*Canter*
10 In which American state is Death Valley?	*California*

Quiz 64
Question 7

Quiz 64
Question 4

Quiz 64 Level 2
General Knowledge

Questions	Answers
1 What H word is the name given to a carriage that carries a coffin at a funeral?	*Hearse*
2 In the film *Mighty Joe Young*, what kind of animal is Joe?	*Gorilla*
3 After which goddess was the capital of Greece named?	*Athena*
4 What was nicknamed a Mae West by U.S. air crew?	*A life jacket*
5 What do you add to blue to make green?	*Yellow*
6 Which bear is called the Lord of the Arctic?	*Polar bear*
7 What instrument is Julian Lloyd Webber famous for playing?	*Cello*
8 Who did the Roundheads fight in the English Civil War?	*Cavaliers*
9 Which English cathedral city shares its name with a shade of green?	*Lincoln*
10 Name the Peter Pan of pop, who had a 1999 No. 1 with "The Millennium Prayer".	*Cliff Richard*

Quiz 63
Question 6

Quiz 63
Question 8

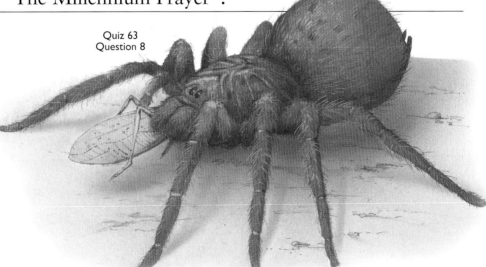

Quiz 65 Level 2
Sport

Questions	Answers
1 Which is not an event in the decathlon: 1500 m, pole vault or triple jump?	*Triple jump*
2 What nationality is motor racing star Jacques Villeneuve?	*Canadian*
3 Which Korean city hosted the 1988 Summer Olympics?	*Seoul*
4 With which sport would you associate the promoter Don King?	Boxing
5 In which sport would you perform an Eskimo roll?	*Canoeing*
6 In September 2001, who scored a hat-trick for England against Germany?	*Michael Owen*
7 What was won four times by Brazil in the 20th century, in 1958, 1962, 1970 and 1994?	*Football's World Cup*
8 In which century were the Wimbledon tennis championships first contested?	*The 19th century*
9 Which Derby winning horse was kidnapped in 1983?	*Shergar*
10 In the U.S. what is played on a gridiron?	*American football*

Quiz 66
Question 5

Quiz 66
Question 1

Quiz 66 Level 2

Sport

Questions	Answers
1 Which sport featured in the film *Cool Runnings*, starring John Candy?	*Bobsleigh*
2 Who was crowned Snooker World Champion in 2001?	*Ronnie O'Sullivan*
3 In 1997 which 21 year old became the youngest winner of golf's U.S. Masters?	*Tiger Woods*
4 Coxless pairs and double sculls are events in which sport?	*Rowing*
5 What did Eddie Charlton carry in 1956 and Muhammed Ali in 1996?	*Olympic torch*
6 In horse racing terms what do the initials S.P. stand for?	*Starting Price*
7 How many players in a netball team?	*Seven*
8 Which former world record-breaking athlete was William Hague's fitness trainer?	*Sebastian Coe*
9 Who was the first French footballer to be voted P.F.A. Player of the Year?	*Eric Cantona*
10 What is the national sport of Ireland?	*Hurling*

Quiz 65
Question 7

Quiz 65
Question 4

Quiz 67 Level 2
General Knowledge

Questions	Answers
1 If you added together a nickel and a dime, how many cents would you have?	*15 (5+10)*
2 What is the main ingredient of the seafood dish Calamari?	*Squid*
3 Who announced, "How tickled he was" to be granted the freedom of the city of Liverpool?	*Ken Dodd*
4 Who played Sgt. Ernie Bilko in the television series?	*Phil Silvers*
5 Des Moines is the capital of which U.S. state?	*Iowa*
6 Who is the patron saint of artists and painters?	*St. Luke*
7 Which Beatle died in November 2001?	*George Harrison*
8 What is the first property that can be bought on a British Monopoly board?	*Old Kent Road*
9 The name of which animal is also one of the seven deadly sins?	*Sloth*
10 In which Irish city was the film *The Commitments* set?	*Dublin*

Quiz 68
Question 1

Quiz 68
Question 4

Questions

Answers

1 Which statue in Copenhagen is named after a Hans Christian Anderson fairy tale?

The Little Mermaid

2 Who composed *The Tales of Hoffmann*?

Offenbach

3 In which H.G. Wells novel was Earth invaded by Martians?

War of the Worlds

4 According to the nonsense verse who "lays its eggs in a paper bag"?

The Cormorant or Shag

5 What alcoholic spirit is the main ingredient in a Moscow Mule cocktail?

Vodka

7 What species of animal is central to the plot of the film *Born Free*?

Lions

6 What star sign follows Taurus?

Gemini

8 What capital city is an anagram of the word mail?

Lima (capital of Peru)

9 From which language did the word fjord originate?

Norwegian

10 What is a blunderbuss?

An old type of gun

Quiz 67
Question 2

Quiz 67
Question 9

Quiz 69 Level 2

Natural World

Questions	Answers
1 What flying insect is known for spreading malaria?	*Mosquito*
2 Do scorpions produce live young or lay eggs?	*Live young*
3 What B word is the name given to the study of plants?	*Botany*
4 What is the more common name for a eucalyptus tree?	*Gum tree*
5 What name is given to a female foal?	*Filly*
6 A Wessex Saddleback is a breed of which farm animal?	*Pig*
7 What breed of dog are most commonly used by Inuits to pull their sledges?	*Husky*
8 What species of snake has varieties called, green tree, reticulated, Indian and Burmese?	*Python*
9 What dog breed connects Beethoven, Schnorbits and the patron saint of mountaineers?	*St. Bernard*
10 A rookery is the name given to a collection of which fast-swimming birds?	*Penguins*

Quiz 70
Question 6

Quiz 70
Question 1

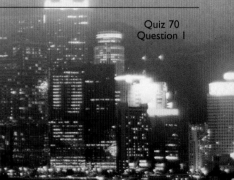

Science and Maths

Questions	Answers
1 What did Thomas Alva Edison invent in 1879 after carrying out 1,200 experiments?	*A light bulb*
2 If a century is divided by a score what is the answer?	*Five (100 divided by 20)*
3 What gas freezes to form dry ice?	*Carbon dioxide*
4 What is one half of a gross?	*72 (144 divided by 2)*
5 How many weeks are there in a century?	*5,200*
6 Enrico Forlanini built the first one in 1905. What was it?	*Hydrofoil*
7 Is the letter I the chemical symbol for iodine, iron or iridium?	*Iodine*
8 If you subtracted a decade from a millennium, how many years would be left?	*990 (1000 – 10)*
9 Which planet would you associate with the chemical symbol of Hg?	*Mercury*
10 How many degrees does a clock's hour hand pass through between 1 a.m. and 6 a.m.?	*150 degrees*

Quiz 69
Question 8

Quiz 69
Question 10

Quiz 71 Level 2

History

Questions

Answers

1 What name was given to the 1086 census of England ordered by William the Conqueror? — *The Domesday Book*

2 What was the name of the ship the Pilgrim Fathers sailed from Devon in 1620? — **The Mayflower**

3 Which Votes for Women organization was founded by Emmeline Pankhurst in 1903? — *The Suffragettes*

4 In 1959 which became the 50th U.S. State? Quiz 72 Question 10 — *Hawaii*

5 Anne Boleyn was the mother of which Queen of England? — *Queen Elizabeth I*

6 In which century did the astrologer Nostradamus live? — *16th century*

7 Who was the first U.S. President to resign from office? — *Richard Nixon*

8 Which Italian artist painted a mural of *The Last Supper* around 1495? — *Leonardo da Vinci*

9 How many Scottish Kings have been called Kenneth: one, two or three? — *Three*

10 Who put his seal on the *Magna Carta* in 1215? — *King John I*

Quiz 72
Question 9

Quiz 72 Level 2

Geography

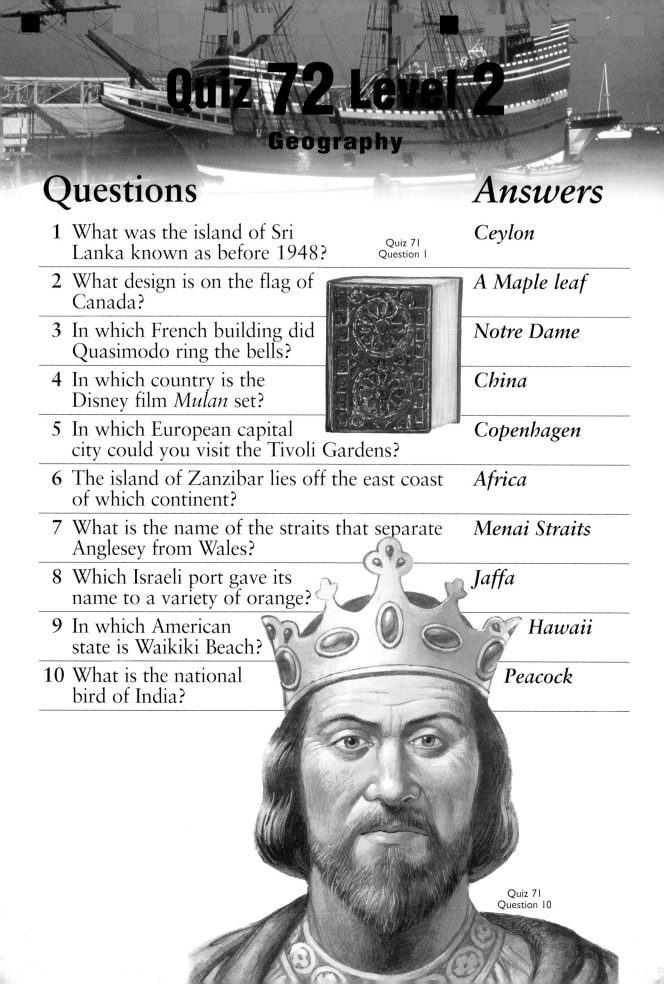

Questions	Answers
1 What was the island of Sri Lanka known as before 1948?	*Ceylon*
2 What design is on the flag of Canada?	*A Maple leaf*
3 In which French building did Quasimodo ring the bells?	*Notre Dame*
4 In which country is the Disney film *Mulan* set?	*China*
5 In which European capital city could you visit the Tivoli Gardens?	*Copenhagen*
6 The island of Zanzibar lies off the east coast of which continent?	*Africa*
7 What is the name of the straits that separate Anglesey from Wales?	*Menai Straits*
8 Which Israeli port gave its name to a variety of orange?	*Jaffa*
9 In which American state is Waikiki Beach?	*Hawaii*
10 What is the national bird of India?	*Peacock*

Quiz 71
Question 1

Quiz 71
Question 10

Quiz 73 Level 2

T.V. and Film

Questions	Answers
1 Name the knighted actor who died in August 2000 and who on film played a Jedi knight.	*Sir Alec Guinness*
2 Who was the child actress who starred in *National Velvet*?	*Elizabeth Taylor*
3 In 1928 who made his film debut in *Plane Crazy*?	*Mickey Mouse*
4 In which city is *A Room with a View* set?	*Florence*
5 Which member of the Addams Family did Christina Ricci play on film?	*Wednesday Addams*
6 On T.V. which monastic sleuth has been portrayed by Sir Derek Jacobi?	*Cadfael*
7 In Rudyard Kipling's *The Jungle Book*, what kind of animal is Shere Khan?	*A tiger*
8 What kind of animal character appeared with Bill and Ben in the children's T.V. series?	*Tortoise (Slowcoach)*
9 In which film did Tommy Lee Jones and Will Smith play agents J and K?	**Men In Black**
10 Who plays the title role in the T.V. series *Ally McBeal*?	*Calista Flockhart*

Quiz 74
Question 7

Quiz 74
Question 9

Quiz 74 Level 2

Music

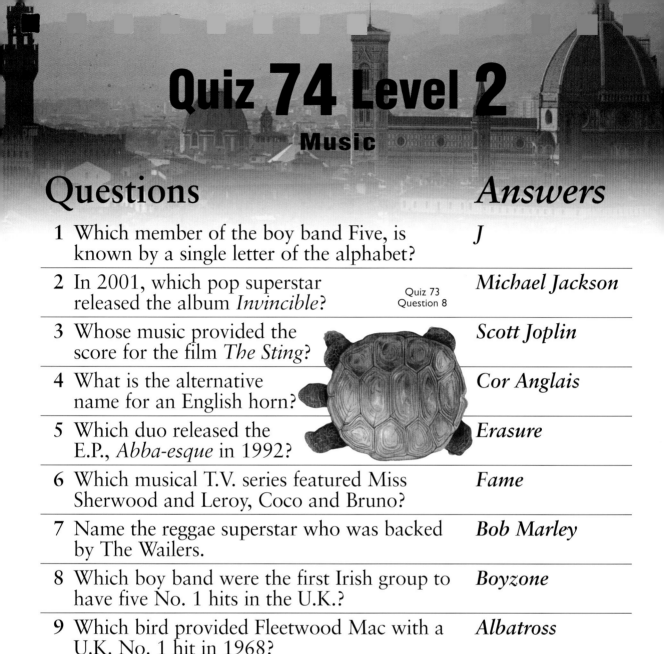

Questions	Answers
1 Which member of the boy band Five, is known by a single letter of the alphabet?	J
2 In 2001, which pop superstar released the album *Invincible*?	Michael Jackson
3 Whose music provided the score for the film *The Sting*?	Scott Joplin
4 What is the alternative name for an English horn?	Cor Anglais
5 Which duo released the E.P., *Abba-esque* in 1992?	Erasure
6 Which musical T.V. series featured Miss Sherwood and Leroy, Coco and Bruno?	Fame
7 Name the reggae superstar who was backed by The Wailers.	Bob Marley
8 Which boy band were the first Irish group to have five No. 1 hits in the U.K.?	Boyzone
9 Which bird provided Fleetwood Mac with a U.K. No. 1 hit in 1968?	Albatross
10 Which group had a No. 1 album in 1994 with *Parklife*?	Blur

Quiz 73
Question 8

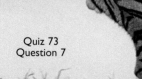

Quiz 73
Question 7

Quiz 75 Level 2
English

Questions	Answers
1 What type of weapon is a scimitar?	*A sword*
2 What P word is the name given to an artist's board on which the paints are mixed?	*Palette*
3 What is the name of the train that takes Harry Potter to the wizard's school?	*Hogwart's Express*
4 What A word is the name given to an animal that can live on land or water?	*Amphibian*
5 What is the silent letter in the word psychiatrist?	*The letter P*
6 According to the saying, what can you not make from a sow's ear?	*A silk purse*
7 If you journeyed by a schooner would you be on a road, at sea or in the air?	*At sea (it is a sailing ship)*
8 What is the first animal mentioned in the nursery rhyme *Hey Diddle Diddle*?	*The cat*
9 What is the plural of court martial?	*Courts martial*
10 What kind of creature is Jeremy Fisher in the Beatrix Potter tales?	*A frog*

Quiz 76
Question 10

Quiz 76
Question 4

Quiz 76 Level 2

Sport

Questions	Answers
1 Which golfer founded his own company called the Great White Shark Company?	*Greg Norman*
2 How many hours long is the Le Mans Endurance Race?	*24 hours*
3 Which sport is played by the Philadelphia Fliers?	*Ice hockey*
4 In which sport would a competitor use a sabre on the piste?	*Fencing*
5 On which river is the Oxford and Cambridge boat race held?	*River Thames*
6 How many rings are there on an archery target?	*Ten*
7 Which Scottish city has been host twice to the Commonwealth Games?	*Edinburgh*
8 In the 20th century how many women ran a sub four-minute mile?	*None*
9 Who was the first Frenchman to become Formula One World Champion?	*Alain Prost*
10 What sport is played by the London Towers?	*Basketball*

Quiz 75
Question 10

Quiz 77 Level 3
General Knowledge

Questions	Answers
1 In which 1991 film did Billy Crystal embark on a cattle drive holiday?	*City Slickers*
2 With which art movement do you associate Salvador Dali?	*The Surrealists*
3 What kind of animal is Mrs Tiggywinkle in the Beatrix Potter tales?	*Hedgehog*
4 *Papillon* is the French word for a what?	*Butterfly*
5 What type of nut provides the flavour of satay sauce?	*Peanut or groundnut*
6 What post did the Archbishop of Krakow take up in 1978?	*The Pope*
7 Saint Mungo is the patron saint of which British city?	*Glasgow*
8 Which American President's portrait appears on a $1bill?	*George Washington*
9 In which American city was the T.V. series *CHiPs* set?	*Los Angeles*
10 Which part of the body is an otoscope used to look into?	*The ear*

Quiz 78
Question 1

Quiz 78
Question 5

Quiz 78 Level 3
General Knowledge

Questions	Answers
1 Who composed *Air on a G String*?	*J.S. Bach*
2 What kind of shop did Margaret Thatcher's father own?	*A grocer's shop*
3 From which animal is cashmere obtained?	*The goat*
4 Who wrote the novel *Sons and Lovers*?	*D.H. Lawrence*
5 What bird is in the title of Harper Lee's famous U.S. novel?	*Mockingbird (To Kill A ...)*
6 What is the metal dial in the middle of a sundial called?	*Gnomon*
7 What title was taken by Prince Edward following his 1999 marriage?	*Earl of Wessex*
8 What event in the Christian calendar is celebrated on Maundy Thursday?	*The Last Supper*
9 The town of Grimsby stands on the estuary of which river?	*Humber*
10 Which country's name is Spanish for rich coast?	*Costa Rica*

Quiz 77
Question 3

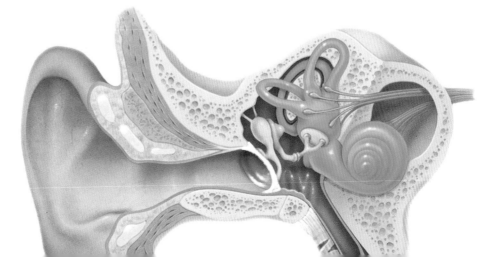

Quiz 77
Question 10

Quiz 79 Level 3
Natural World

Questions	Answers
1 Which cartoon character was always trying to make a meal out of Road Runner?	*Wile E Coyote*
2 What leaves provide the staple diet of koala bears?	*Eucalyptus*
3 A male donkey is called a Jack. Which girl's name provides the name of a female donkey?	*Jenny*
4 Which stinging creature represents one of the signs of the Zodiac?	*Scorpion (Scorpio)*
5 Which Portugese word does the dodo derive its name from, is it flightless, stupid or dead?	*Stupid*
6 What species of monkey gave its name to a protein found in blood?	*Rhesus monkey*
7 Is a boomslang a frog, a snake or a bird of prey?	*A venomous tree snake*
8 Brock is another name for which carnivorous mammal?	*Badger*
9 Which animal's name means little thief in Latin?	*Ferret*
10 How many legs does a lobster have?	*Ten*

Quiz 80
Question 9

Quiz 80
Question 6

Quiz 80 Level 3
History

Questions	Answers
1 Does the Australian dingo bark?	No (it howls)
2 What has the shorter snout: an alligator or a crocodile?	Alligator
3 Sloes are the fruit of which tree?	Blackthorn
4 The fallabella is the world's smallest breed of what?	Horse
5 What is the largest species of cat native to South America?	Jaguar
6 A labour is the collective name given to a group of which burrowing animals?	Moles
7 Which rhino has only one horn? The black, white, Sumatran or Indian rhino?	Indian
8 A carapace is the technical term for the shell of which creatures?	Tortoise family
9 What type of bird is the main ingredient of squab pie?	Pigeon
10 Which fungal disease of elm trees do bark beetles spread?	Dutch elm disease

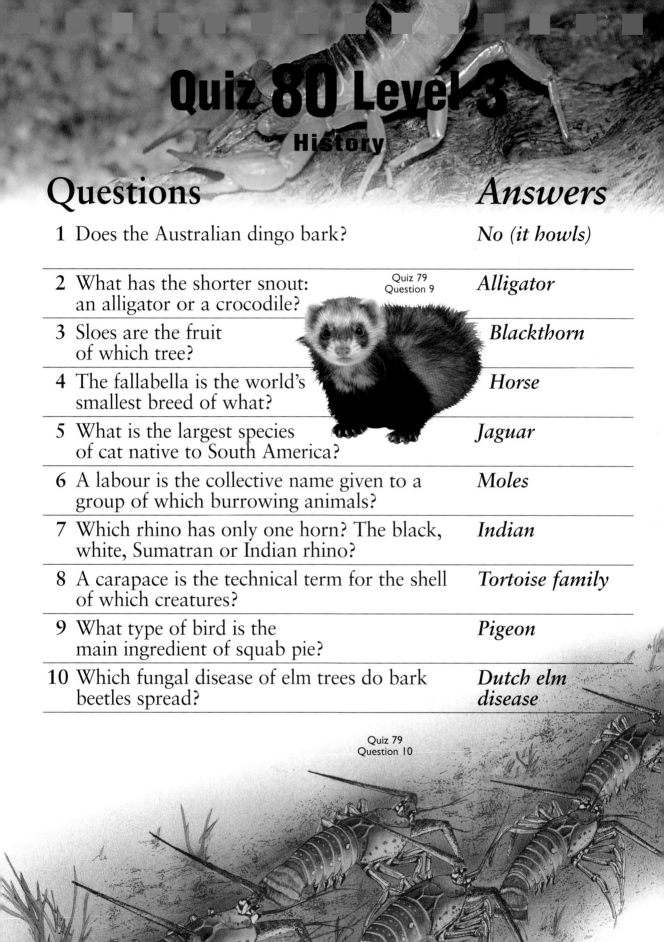

Quiz 79
Question 9

Quiz 79
Question 10

Quiz 81 Level 3
General Knowledge

Questions	Answers
1 What are espadrilles?	*Canvas shoes with cord soles*
2 Which Greek mythological hero killed the gorgon Medusa?	*Perseus*
3 What is the name of a female salmon?	*Hen*
4 Which actor led the seven in *The Magnificent Seven*?	*Yul Brynner*
5 In which country is Shakespeare's *Hamlet* set?	*Denmark*
6 On which river does Le Havre stand?	*River Seine*
7 In what year was O.J. Simpson found not guilty of murder?	*1995*
8 He was played on stage by David Essex and on film by Antonio Banderas. Who was he?	*Che Guevara*
9 Who was the servant of the literary character Don Quixote?	*Sancho Panza*
10 Which German town was the birthplace of Henry VIII's fourth wife?	*Cleves*

Quiz 82
Question 6

Quiz 82
Question 7

Questions	Answers
1 According to Mattel, Barbie's manufacturers, her surname is Richards, Roberts or Riley?	*Roberts*
2 In which country is the source of the River Amazon?	*Peru*
3 What is the national flower of Sweden?	*Lily of the valley*
4 Which planet was named after the Roman Goddess of love?	*Venus*
5 Which biblical character's name beginning with J, is now used to describe a scheming woman?	*Jezebel*
6 What kind of creature was Rikki Tikki Tavi's adversary?	*A cobra*
7 By what other name is the animal the suricate known?	*Meerkat*
8 What sea lies between Australia and New Zealand?	*Tasman Sea*
9 Name the English artist who is famed for painting Californian swimming pools?	*David Hockney*
10 How many sides has a icosahedron?	*Twenty*

Quiz 81
Question 5

Quiz 81
Question 8

Quiz 83 Level 3
General Knowledge

Questions	Answers
1 Which girl's first name is the Italian word for woman?	*Donna*
2 Who directed the film *The Good, the Bad and the Ugly?*	*Sergio Leone*
3 Which famous statue stands high above Rio de Janeiro?	*Christ the Redeemer*
4 Who did Elijah Wood play in the film *The Lord Of The Rings?*	*Frodo*
5 Which monarch has been played by Charles Laughton, Sid James and Richard Burton?	*Henry VIII*
6 What is the surname of Heathcliff's adopted family in the novel *Wuthering Heights?*	*Earnshaw*
7 Which satirical magazine celebrated its 40th birthday in October 2001?	**Private Eye**
8 What is the cubed root of one million?	*100 (100 x 100 x 100 = 1 million)*
9 Who is the Greek Goddess of love?	*Aphrodite*
10 Who is the Supreme God of Norse mythology?	*Odin*

Quiz 84
Question 10

Quiz 84
Question 2

Quiz 84 Level 3
General Knowledge

Questions	Answers
1 Which country and western singer starred in the film *9 to 5*?	*Dolly Parton*
2 In which American state is Amarillo?	*Texas*
3 Artists Diego Rivera and Frida Kahlo came from which country?	*Mexico*
4 Coach dog is an alternative name for which breed of dog?	*Dalmatian*
5 What is another name for Darbur Sihab, the most sacred temple in the Sikh religion?	*The Golden Temple*
6 What is the alternative name for the Decalogue in the Bible?	*The Ten Commandments*
7 What is the nearest country to the North Pole?	*Greenland*
8 What is a Moorish idol?	*A tropical fish*
9 Which Australian city was named in honour of the consort of William IV?	*Adelaide*
10 Which Venetian traveller spent 17 years in the service of Kublai Khan?	*Marco Polo*

Quiz 83
Question 10

Quiz 83
Question 5

Quiz 85 Level 3
General Knowledge

Questions	Answers
1 Approximately two miles in length, what is the name of the main canal in Venice?	*Grand Canal*
2 Caviar is obtained from the roe of which fish?	*Sturgeon*
3 In which century was Thomas Beckett murdered?	*12th century*
4 Which country has the longest coastline in Europe?	*Norway*
5 The title of which Shakespeare play is also the name for a small village?	*Hamlet*
6 The American drama series *The West Wing*, is mainly set in which U.S. building?	*The White House*
7 From which country did Brazil gain its independence in 1822?	*Portugal*
8 Name the actress who was the first wife of Ronald Reagan.	*Jane Wyman*
9 Name the comic strip hero from Mega City One, played on film by Sylvester Stallone?	*Judge Dredd*
10 What animal would you associate with February 2nd in the U.S.?	*Groundhog (Day)*

Quiz 86
Question 9

Quiz 86
Question 7

Quiz 86 Level 3
General Knowledge

Questions	Answers
1 Which organ of the body produces bile?	*Liver*
2 In which language was the Domesday Book written?	*Latin*
3 What name is given to the central stone of an arch?	*Keystone*
4 In which park is Princess Diana buried?	*Althorp Park*
5 Which shellfish produces pearls?	*Oyster*
6 Which London theatre, opened in 1871, was named after Queen Victoria's husband?	*The Royal Albert Hall*
7 Which anniversary is celebrated after one year of marriage?	*Paper*
8 Which C word is the medical term for gristle in the human body?	*Cartilage*
9 Tiger Tom and Alicante are both varieties of what?	*Tomatoes*
10 Qantas is the national airline of which country?	*Australia*

Quiz 85
Question 4

Quiz 85
Question 2

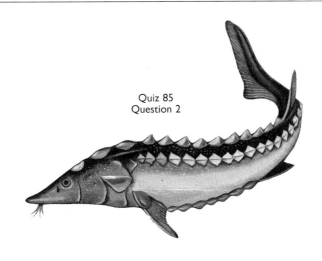

Quiz 87 Level 3
Science and Maths

Questions
Answers

1 What is the alternative name for fruit sugar? — *Fructose*

2 Which part of the body is affected by glaucoma? — *Eyes*

3 Which metal is also known as wolfram? — *Tungsten*

Quiz 88
Question 4

4 In mathematics, Calculus is named after the Latin for what? — *Pebble*

5 Mg is the chemical symbol for which element? — *Magnesium*

6 Charon is which planet's only moon? — *Pluto*

7 What unit of measurement is equivalent to one million tons of T.N.T.? — *Megaton*

8 What did Wilhelm C. Roentgen discover in 1895? — *X rays*

9 How is 70 written in Roman numerals? — *LXX*

10 What is one tenth of a bel? — *Decibel*

Quiz 88
Question 1

Quiz 88 Level 3
Science and Maths

Questions	Answers
1 What part of the body is affected by dermatitis?	*Skin*
2 By what other name is the plant deadly nightshade also known?	*Belladonna*
3 In mathematics what can be complex, mixed or vulgar?	*Fractions*
4 In August 1999, what phenomenon occurred in the daytime sky?	*Total solar eclipse*
5 From what flowers are vanilla pods obtained?	*Orchids*
6 What name is given to the study of the mechanics of movement in living creatures?	*Biomechanics*
7 Which gas has the atomic number of 8?	*Oxygen*
8 What nationality was the botanist and taxonomist Carolus Linneaus?	*Swedish*
9 Divide the number of degrees in a semi-circle by the number of degrees in a triangle?	*One (180 divided by 180)*
10 What symbol represents the ratio of the circumference of a circle to the diameter?	*Pi*

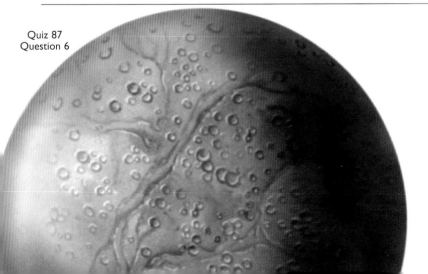

Quiz 87
Question 6

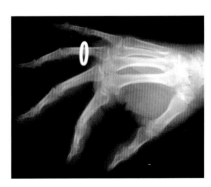

Quiz 87
Question 8

Quiz 89 Level 3
General Knowledge

Questions	Answers
1 Who is the heroine in *The Merchant of Venice*? Is it Cordelia, Portia or Desdemona?	*Portia*
2 Whose death warrant did Elizabeth I sign in February 1587?	*Mary, Queen of Scots*
3 Who provided the animations for the *Monty Python* T.V. show?	*Terry Gilliam*
4 Name the famous inventor played by Michael Redgrave in the film *The Dam Busters*?	*Barnes Wallis*
5 What is obtained by crossing a tangerine with a grapefruit?	*Ugli fruit*
6 Which famous American folk singer wrote the song "Mighty Quinn"?	*Bob Dylan*
7 From which art gallery was the *Mona Lisa* stolen in 1911?	*The Louvre*
8 A supernova marks the end of the lifetime of a what?	*A star*
9 Which famous novelist was born Eric Arthur Blair?	*George Orwell*
10 In which country is Mount Eiger?	*Switzerland*

Quiz 90
Question 6

Quiz 90
Question 7

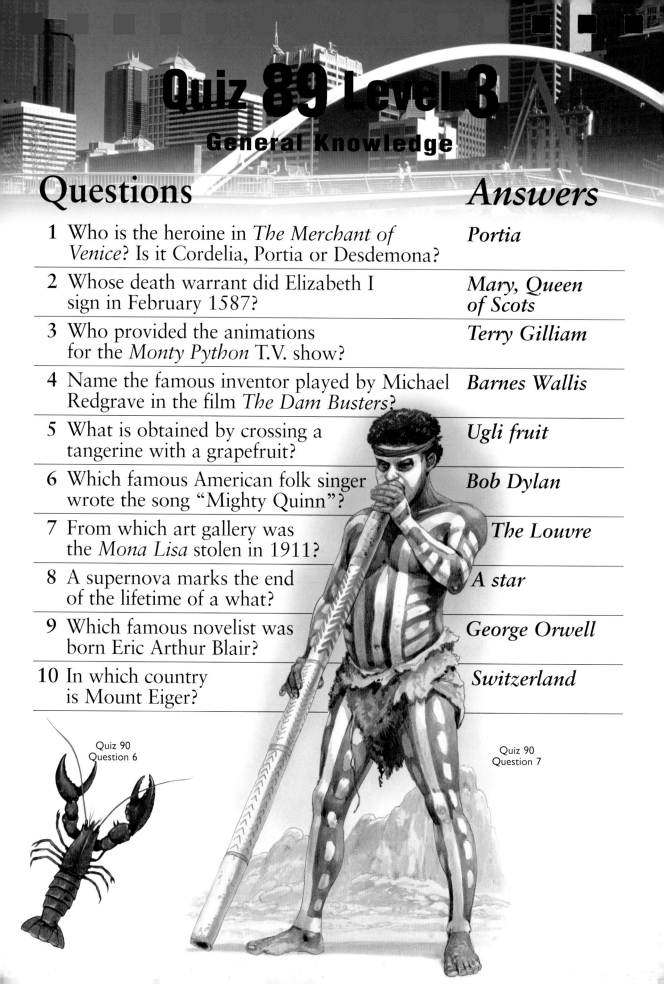

Quiz 9U Level 3

General Knowledge

Questions	Answers
1 In which decade of the 20th century was the Suez crisis?	*1950s*
2 The novel *Catch 22*, was set during which war?	*World War II*
3 Which vitamin is also known as ascorbic acid?	*Vitamin C*
4 Which actress was born Julia Wells?	*Julie Andrews*
5 Which island was the home of T.V. detective Jim Bergerac?	*Jersey*
6 What sea creature has species called European, Norway, Spiny and American?	*Lobster*
7 What is the name of the long, Australian wind instrument, that makes a low droning sound?	*Didgeridoo*
8 In which film did Hugh Grant play bookshop owner William Thacker?	Notting Hill
9 Which member of the British Royal Family was born in September 1984?	*Prince Harry*
10 What is the name of the statue in Brussels that is nicknamed Brussels oldest citizen?	*Mannekin Pis*

Quiz 89
Question 2

Quiz 89
Question 8

Quiz 91 Level 3

Geography

Questions	Answers
1 Rudolph Hess was the last prisoner to be held in which building in England's capital?	*The Tower of London*
2 In which country is the most westerly point of South America?	*Peru*
3 What type of plant features on the flag of Mexico?	*Cactus*
4 In which ocean are the Maldives?	*The Indian Ocean*
5 In which city was Christopher Columbus born?	*Genoa*
6 What country would you be visiting if you spent a dirham in the capital city of Rabat?	*Morocco*
7 Hammerfest, Europe's most northerly town, lies in which country?	*Norway*
8 In which European country is the headquarters of the Heineken Brewing Company?	*Holland*
9 In which country is the source of the River Rhine?	*Switzerland*
10 What is the largest province in Canada?	*Quebec*

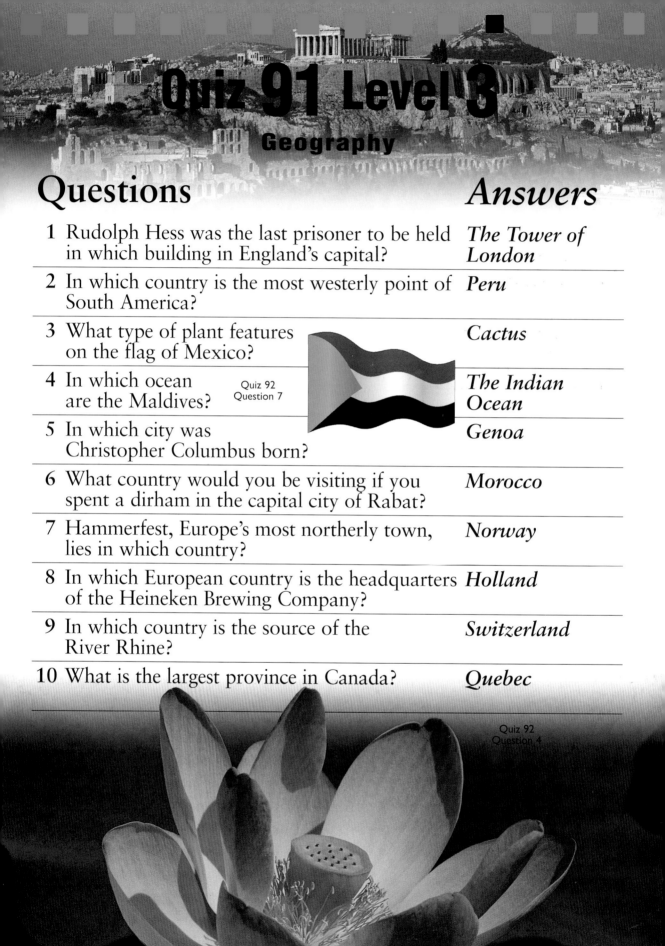

Quiz 92
Question 7

Quiz 92
Question 4

Quiz 92 Level 3
Geography

Questions	Answers
1 Which European capital city has an old quarter called the Plaka?	*Athens*
2 What is the state capital of Texas?	*Austin*
3 Which country is nearest to the Greek island of Rhodes?	*Turkey*
4 What is the national flower of India?	*Lotus*
5 Which African country gained independence from Britain in 1962?	*Uganda*
6 In which U.S. state is the city of Tucson?	*Arizona*
7 Khartoum is the capital of which African country?	*Sudan*
8 What is the name of Japan's largest island?	*Honshu*
9 Which European capital city lies mainly on the island of Zealand?	*Copenhagen*
10 Which English city did the Romans call Aquae Sulis?	*Bath*

Quiz 91
Question 3

Quiz 93 Level 3

General Knowledge

Questions	Answers
1 Who played Rocky Cassidy in the T.V. series *Boon*?	*Neil Morrisey*
2 Which wild west outlaw was the subject of a hit by Cher in 1990?	*Jesse James*
3 What Arctic mammal is also the heraldic name for black?	*Sable*
4 What famous building near Paris, contains the famous Hall of Mirrors?	*Palace of Versailles*
5 Who was the song "Matchstick Men and Matchstick Cats and Dogs" a tribute to?	*L.S. Lowry*
6 Which pop group provided the music for the 1980 film *Flash Gordon*?	*Queen*
7 Which Alaskan mountain, named after a U.S. President, is the highest in North America?	*Mount McKinley*
8 What major film company has a logo known as The Proud Lady?	*Columbia*
9 The cities of Belgrade and Budapest both stand on which river?	*Danube*
10 How many eggs are there in six and a half dozen?	*78*

Quiz 94
Question 3

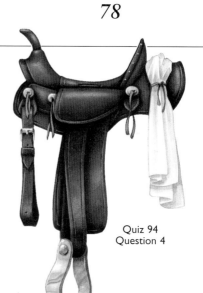

Quiz 94
Question 4

Quiz 94 Level 3
General Knowledge

Questions	Answers
1 Is kahlua liqueur coffee flavoured, orange flavoured or mint flavoured?	*Coffee*
2 Who flew in a plane called *The Spirit of St. Louis*?	*Charles Lindbergh*
3 From which fruit is the brandy slivovitz made: is it pears, plums or pineapple?	*Plums*
4 What is the name for a horse rider's foot support suspended from the saddle?	*Stirrup*
5 Which English artist's father owned Flatford Mill?	*John Constable*
6 In which country was the environmental organization Greenpeace founded?	*Canada*
7 What wedding anniversary is celebrated by 40 years of marriage?	*Ruby*
8 Who in 1477 produced the first book printed in England?	*William Caxton*
9 What rank of nobility comes directly below an Earl?	*Viscount*
10 What is the alternative name for Beethoven's 3rd Symphony?	*Eroica*

Quiz 93
Question 2

Quiz 95 Level 3
English

Questions	Answers
1 What is the collective name for a group of angels?	*Host*
2 Which book featured Meg, Jo, Beth and Amy March?	*Little Women*
3 What is the English equivalent of what the Americans call vests?	*Waistcoat*
4 Which American writer wrote *The Grapes of Wrath*?	*John Steinbeck*
5 Which famous diarist finished each entry with the words "and so to bed"?	*Samuel Pepys*
6 Beginning with K, what is the name of the Indian drama consisting of dance and music?	*Kathakali*
7 What is the name of rocky and metallic objects orbiting the Sun, also know as minor planets?	*Asteroids*
8 What do you call a word having the same sound or spelling as another?	*A homonym*
9 Does the word festinate mean tasty or hasty?	*Hasty*
10 Who wrote the poem *Paradise Lost*?	*John Milton*

Quiz 96
Question 2

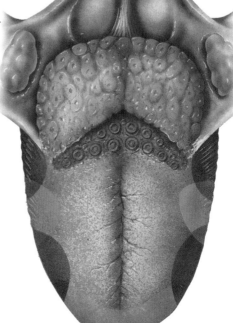

Quiz 96
Question 1

Quiz 96 Level 3
English

Questions	Answers
1 What part of the body is affected by glossitis?	*The tongue*
2 What name is shared by a heavy spiked club and the spice made from nutmeg?	*Mace*
3 What A word describes a circular coral reef growing on top of a submerged mountain?	*Atoll*
4 What F word is the name given to the metal ribs on the fingerboard of a guitar?	*Frets*
5 What is the name of the sequel to *Bridget Jones's Diary*?	**The Edge of Reason**
6 What king was portrayed by Shakespeare as a murderous hunchback?	*Richard III*
7 Eugenics is the study of what?	*Selective breeding*
8 If a meeting is held *sub rosa* what does this mean?	*In secret*
9 How much is a person paid for an honorary post?	*Nothing*
10 In which city is *Romeo and Juliet* set?	*Verona*

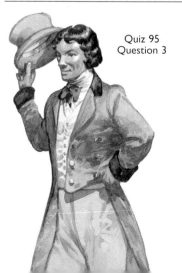

Quiz 95
Question 3

Quiz 95
Question 6

Quiz 97 Level 3
General Knowledge

Questions	Answers
1 Who did Dana International represent when winning the Eurovision Song Contest?	*Israel*
2 What I word was the name of the title given to the daughter of a Spanish king?	*Infanta*
3 In what country outside of India, would you find the largest Hindu temple?	*England*
4 In the United States what is the Republican Party's symbol?	*An elephant*
5 Who won a Best Actress Oscar for her role in *Erin Brockovich*?	*Julia Roberts*
6 Which French King was known as The Sun King?	*Louis XIV (Louis 14th)*
7 What is Che Guevara's real first name?	*Ernesto*
8 In what year did Richard Branson found Virgin Atlantic Airlines: 1982, 1984 or 1986?	*1984*
9 Which plant, native to the Carolinas, lures insects with its nectar into deadly sprung traps?	*Venus flytrap*
10 What food is nicknamed the bread of Mexico?	*Tortilla*

Quiz 98
Question 6

Quiz 98
Question 10

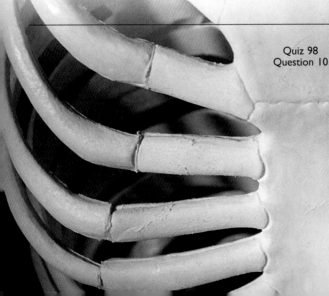

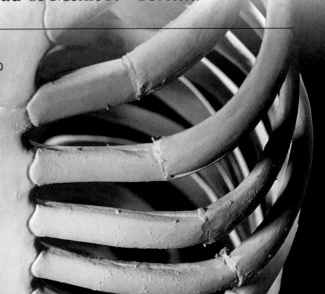

Questions	Answers
1 What novel opens with the line "The great fish moved silently through the water"?	*Jaws*
2 What is the name of the main river running through Hamburg?	*Elbe*
3 Which movie actress is the mother of the actress Kate Hudson?	*Goldie Hawn*
4 What title did Robert Runcie hold between 1980 and 1990?	*Archbishop of Canterbury*
5 The Christian Mission was the original name for which army?	*Salvation Army*
6 What types of berries are used to flavour the alcoholic spirit gin?	*Juniper berries*
7 What Japanese delicacy is considered to be the world's most dangerous food?	*The fugu fish*
8 Which famous author received a knighthood for his medical services during the Boer War?	*Sir Arthur Conan Doyle*
9 What is the name of the largest castle in Wales?	*Caerphilly*
10 What are there 12 pairs of in the human body?	*Ribs*

Quiz 97
Question 6

Quiz 97
Question 9

Questions	Answers
1 Who did Kenneth Williams play in the film *Carry On Cleo*?	*Julius Caesar*
2 In the *Addams Family* what is the name of the uncle?	*Fester*
3 Who played Eva Peron in the film *Evita* directed by Alan Parker?	*Madonna*
4 Name the actor who played Chief Engineer Scott in *Star Trek*?	*James Doohan*
5 Who played the villain Harvey Two Face, in the 1995 film *Batman Forever*?	*Tommy Lee Jones*
6 Which Belgian actor played a time-travelling law enforcer in the film *Timecop*?	*Jean-Claude Van Damme*
7 In what was Jock Ewing travelling when he was killed in the T.V. soap *Dallas*?	*Helicopter*
8 Which female criminal was the subject of the film *Dance With A Stranger*?	*Ruth Ellis*
9 Which author wrote the dramas *Pennies From Heaven* and *The Singing Detective*?	*Dennis Potter*
10 Who is married to Brad Pitt?	*Jennifer Aniston*

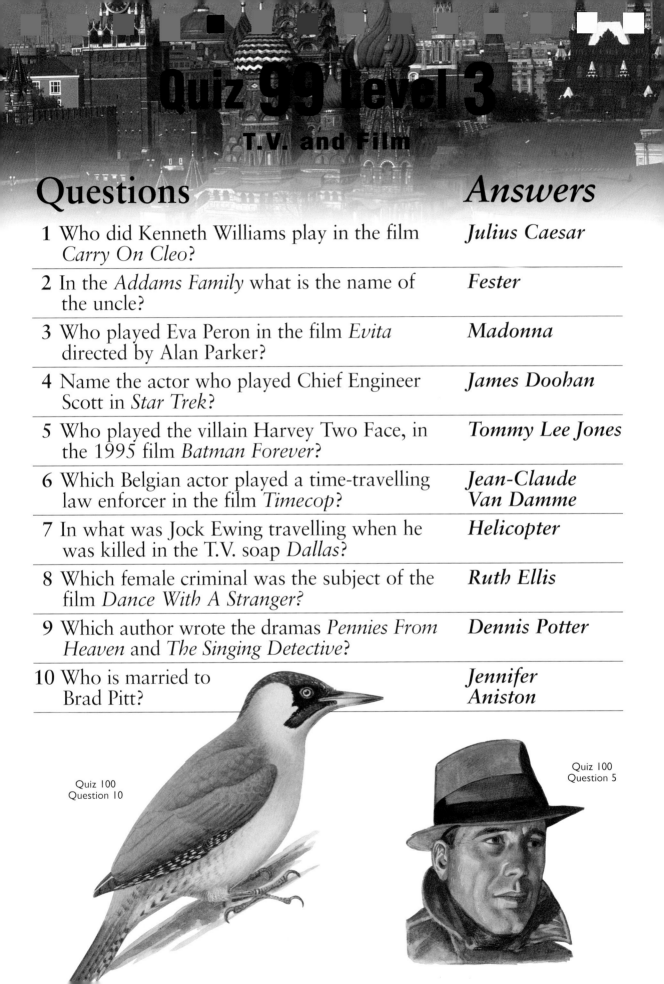

Quiz 100
Question 10

Quiz 100
Question 5

Quiz 100 Level 3
T.V. and Film

Questions	Answers
1 If Pokemon means pocket monsters, what does Digimon mean?	*Digital monsters*
2 Which actress connects the films *The Accused*, *Bugsy Malone* and *Taxi Driver*?	*Jodie Foster*
3 Name the actor who plays Hagrid in *Harry Potter and the Philosopher's Stone*?	*Robbie Coltrane*
4 In which 1993 film blockbuster did Sam Neil play Dr Alan Grant?	**Jurassic Park**
5 Who played boat owner Charlie Allnut in the film *The African Queen*?	*Humphrey Bogart*
6 In which country was *Dr Zhivago* set?	*Russia*
7 In the T.V. series *Bonanza* what was the name of the Cartwright family's ranch?	*Ponderosa*
8 In which 1987 film did Michael Douglas play stockbroker Gordon Gecko?	**Wall Street**
9 Who provided the voice of Z-4195 in the 1998 film *Antz*?	*Woody Allen*
10 Which bird inspired Walter Lantz to create his famous cartoon character Woody?	*A woodpecker*

Quiz 99
Question 7

Quiz 99
Question 1

Quiz 101 Level 3

General Knowledge

Questions	Answers
1 What name is given to the period of 40 days before Easter?	*Lent*
2 Oil of vitriol is an alternative name for which acid?	*Sulphuric Acid*
3 Which literary bogeyman did Raymond Briggs create?	*Fungus the Bogeyman*
4 Who wrote the novel *Dracula*?	*Bram Stoker*
5 How many sides do the majority of snowflakes have?	*Six*
6 Which is the hottest planet in our solar system?	*Mercury*
7 Which Macedonian leader was victorious in the Battle of Issus in 333BC?	*Alexander the Great*
8 Which infamous couple was shot dead in an ambush in May 1934?	*Bonnie and Clyde*
9 How many stripes are on the Star Spangled Banner?	*Thirteen*

Quiz 102
Question 4

Quiz 102
Question 1

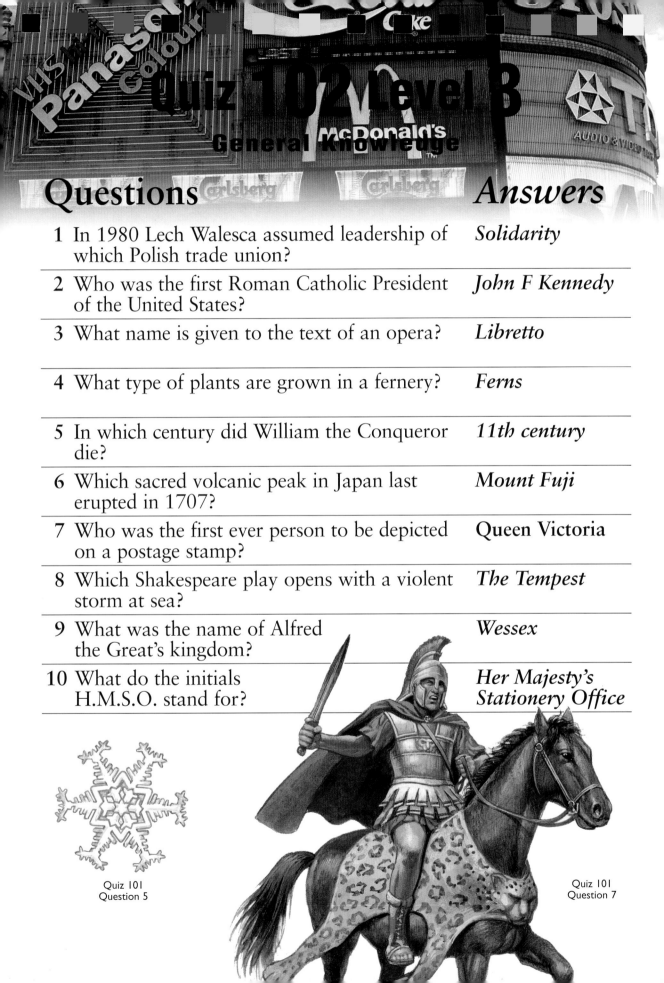

Quiz 102 Level 3
General Knowledge

Questions	Answers
1 In 1980 Lech Walesca assumed leadership of which Polish trade union?	*Solidarity*
2 Who was the first Roman Catholic President of the United States?	*John F Kennedy*
3 What name is given to the text of an opera?	*Libretto*
4 What type of plants are grown in a fernery?	*Ferns*
5 In which century did William the Conqueror die?	*11th century*
6 Which sacred volcanic peak in Japan last erupted in 1707?	*Mount Fuji*
7 Who was the first ever person to be depicted on a postage stamp?	**Queen Victoria**
8 Which Shakespeare play opens with a violent storm at sea?	*The Tempest*
9 What was the name of Alfred the Great's kingdom?	*Wessex*
10 What do the initials H.M.S.O. stand for?	*Her Majesty's Stationery Office*

Quiz 101
Question 5

Quiz 101
Question 7

Questions

	Questions	Answers
1	Who was the first footballer to be voted B.B.C. Sports Personality of the Year?	*Bobby Moore*
2	What was the venue of the 2002 Winter Olympics?	*Salt Lake City*
3	What do the initials T.T. stand for in the Isle of Man T.T. Races?	*Tourist Trophy*
4	What is the name of Minnesota's American football team?	*Minnesota Vikings*
5	Which hat-trick hero wrote the book *1966 And All That*?	*Geoff Hurst*
6	In basketball, how high are the hoop and net above the ground?	*3.05 m/10 ft*
7	The term highly strung, originated in which sport?	*Archery*
8	In Formula 1 racing what does a red and yellow striped flag mean?	*Slippery track*
9	In what year was Damon Hill crowned Formula 1 World Champion?	*1996*
10	What piece of apparatus for a female gymnast is 5 m/6 ft 6 ins long?	*The beam*

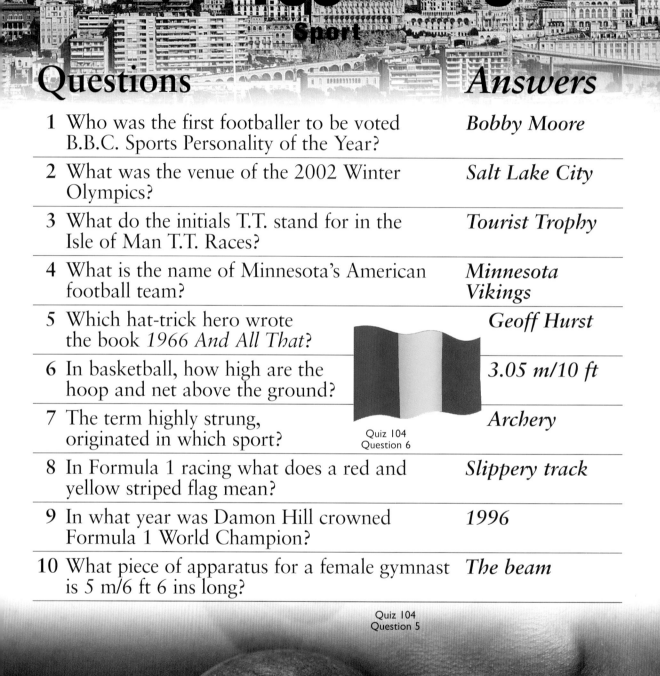

Quiz 104
Question 6

Quiz 104
Question 5

Quiz 104 Level 3

Sport

Questions	Answers
1 In a baseball game, how many innings does each team have?	*Nine*
2 Which famous footballer from the past was nicknamed the Wizard of Dribble?	*Sir Stanley Matthews*
3 Which ball sport is played on an area 30.5 m/100 ft long and 15.25m/50 ft wide?	*Netball*
4 In judo, which belt follows the Yellow Belt?	*Orange*
5 In which sport do men throw a 7.26 kg/16lb ball, and women one weighing 4 kg/8lb 8oz?	*Shot put*
6 Which country did gymnast Nadia Comaneci represent when she scored the first perfect *10.00*?	*Romania*
7 The Monaco Grand Prix is staged around the winding streets of which town?	*Monte Carlo*
8 Which is older, the London or New York Marathon?	*New York*
9 Which tennis player is nicknamed the Swiss Miss?	*Martina Hingis*
10 What is the nationality of the athlete Said Aouita?	*Moroccan*

Quiz 103
Question 10

Quiz 103
Question 4

Quiz 105 Level 3
General Knowledge

Questions	Answers
1 What type of animal was Clint Eastwood's co-star in the film *Every Which Way But Loose*?	*Orang-utan*
2 What five-letter C word is the name given to the dried kernel of a coconut?	*Copra*
3 Which famous violin maker lived in Cremona, Italy?	*Antonio Stradivari*
4 Which Greek island, also the name of a lettuce, was the home of Hippocrates?	*Kos or Cos*
5 What H word is the name of a cushion that is knelt on in church?	*Hassock*
6 What phobia did Little Miss Muffet suffer from?	*Arachnophobia (a fear of spiders)*
7 Chardonnay and Liebfraumilch are both types of what?	*White wine*
8 Which two elements make up sand?	*Oxygen and silicon*
9 What is pyrophobia the fear of?	*Fire*
10 What is the capital city of Albania?	*Tirana*

Quiz 106
Question 8

Quiz 106
Question 4

Quiz 106 Level 3
Music

Questions	Answers
1 Who had a posthumous U.K. No 1 in 1993 with the song "Living On My Own"?	*Freddie Mercury*
2 A sackbut was the old name for which of the following: trumpet, tuba or trombone?	*Trombone*
3 In which year was Britney Spears born?	*1981*
4 Which song written by Neil Diamond was a U.K. No 1 hit for UB40 in 1983?	*"Red, Red Wine"*
5 In October 2001 which Rolling Stone qualified for his old age pension?	*Bill Wyman*
6 Who composed the song, "Land of Hope and Glory"?	*Edward Elgar*
7 In which country was Cliff Richard born?	*India*
8 In *The Muppet Show*, what instrument is played by Zoot?	*Saxophone*
9 The song "Lady Marmalade", featured in which 2001 film starring Nicole Kidman?	Moulin Rouge
10 Stevie Nicks and Christine McVie are the female members of which group?	*Fleetwood Mac*

Quiz 105
Question 7

Quiz 105
Question 1

Quiz 107 Level 3
T.V. and Film

Questions	Answers
1 Who did Kurt Russell play in the film *Tombstone*?	*Wyatt Earp*
2 In which T.V. series did Wendy Craig play Nicholas Lyndhurst's mother?	**Butterflies**
3 The actress Holly Hunter won an Oscar for her role in which 1993 film?	**The Piano**
4 In which film did Russell Crowe play Maximus Decimus Meridus ?	**Gladiator**
5 In which 1997 film did Harrison Ford play President James Marshall?	**Airforce One**
6 Who directed the 2001 film *Gosford Park*?	*Robert Altman*
7 Who starred in the lead role in the film *Educating Rita*?	*Julie Walters*
8 In *Brideshead Revisited* what was Sebastian Flyte's special companion Aloysius?	*A teddy bear*
9 What is the name of Roseanne's sister in the T.V. series *Roseanne*?	*Jackie*
10 What was the name of the character played by George Clooney in T.V.'s *ER*?	*Dr. Doug Ross*

Quiz 108
Question 4

Quiz 108
Question 1

Quiz 108 Level 3

General Knowledge

Questions	Answers
1 From the 12th to the 19th century what name was given to the Japanese warrior class?	*Samurai*
2 Which world leader, who died in 1953, had a name meaning Man of Steel?	*Stalin*
3 Name the famous explorer who married Elizabeth Throckmorton.	*Sir Walter Raleigh*
4 In 1798 an additional verse was added to the British National Anthem in honour of whom?	*Horatio Nelson*
5 What is the fifth book of the Bible?	*Deuteronomy*
6 What is the name for the chest cavity?	*Thorax*
7 Michael Jordan played basketball for which team?	*Chicago Bulls*
8 Where would you see Cookie Monster and Big Bird?	Sesame Street
9 What does the word karaoke literally mean?	*Empty orchestra*
10 Name the capital of Iceland?	*Reykjavik*

Quiz 107
Question 8

Quiz 107
Question 4

Quiz 109 Level 3
Geography

Questions	Answers
1 What was the name of the giant statue on the island of Rhodes that was dedicated to Zeus?	*Colossus of Rhodes*
2 Damask is a type of woven fabric that took its name from which city?	*Damascus*
3 What is the national flower of Austria?	*Eidelweiss*
4 What is the most highly populated city in China?	*Shanghai*
5 By area what is the largest country in Africa?	*Sudan*
6 In which Asian city would you shop in an area called the Ginza?	*Tokyo*
7 What breed of cat was named after the former name of Ethiopia?	*Abyssinian (Abyssinia)*
8 Which African country takes its name from the Spanish for lion mountains?	*Sierra Leone*
9 In 1948 the Faroe Islands gained independence from which European country?	*Denmark*
10 In which South American country is the world's highest capital city La Paz found?	*Bolivia*

Quiz 110
Question 10

Quiz 110
Question 1

Questions	Answers
1 What was the extremely handy sporting invention of Jack Broughton?	*Boxing gloves*
2 Which ice skater won a gold medal for Britain in the 1976 Winter Olympics?	*John Curry*
3 How many points are scored on the black ball if a snooker player makes a 147 break?	*112*
4 Name the first woman to win five medals for athletics in the same Olympic Games?	*Marion Jones (Sydney 2000)*
5 2001 Formula 1 World Champion, Michael Schumacher, drove for which team?	*Ferrari*
6 How long does a chukka last in a game of Polo?	*7 minutes*
7 How many periods of play are there in an ice hockey match?	*Three (20 minutes each)*
8 What is the usual term for a golf course by the sea?	*Golf links*
9 In which equestrian discipline might you see piaffe, serpentine and passage movements?	*Dressage*
10 Lady Paramount was the name given to an official of which sport?	*Archery*

Quiz 109
Question 7

Quiz 109
Question 4

Quiz 111 Level 3
English

Questions	Answers
1 Who was the author of *For Whom the Bell Tolls*?	**Ernest Hemmingway**
2 What name is given to a line on a map that connects points of the same height?	*Contour*
3 *West Side Story* is based on which play by Shakespeare?	**Romeo and Juliet**
4 Name Dorothy's dog in the *The Wonderful Wizard of Oz*?	*Toto*
5 What is the only letter that is worth five points in Scrabble, is it J, K or V?	*K*
6 Who wrote the novel *Bridget Jones's Diary*?	**Helen Fielding**
7 What is studied by an icthyologist?	*Fish*
8 Where are Armistead Maupin's *Tales of the City* series set?	**San Francisco**
9 In the James Bond novels who is his boss?	*M*
10 What was the name of the captain in pursuit of Moby Dick?	*Captain Ahab*

Quiz 112
Question 9

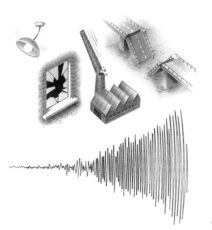

Quiz 112
Question 7

Quiz 112 Level 3
Science and Maths

Questions	Answers
1 Was the first electronic calculator manufactured in 1953, 1963 or 1973?	*1963*
2 Brimstone is the old name for which element?	*Sulphur*
3 How many minutes are there in three and a third hours?	*200*
4 What letter represents 1000 in Roman numerals?	*M*
5 What do the lachrymal glands produce?	*Tears*
6 How are chlorofluorocarbons emissions more commonly known?	*CFC gasses*
7 What is measured on the Richter Scale?	*Earthquakes*
8 What branch of mathematics is concerned with sines and co-sines?	*Trigonometry*
9 What mode of transport was invented by Christopher Cockerill?	*Hovercraft*
10 What is removed from dehydrated food?	*Water*

Quiz 111
Question 7

Quiz 111
Question 1

Questions	Answers
1 Which part of a flower contains the pollen?	*Anther*
2 What is a male badger called?	*Boar*
3 What are the only birds to moult their beaks?	*Puffin*
4 On a horse, is the fetlock on the tail, on the leg or on the withers?	*On the leg*
5 What equine creature has species called Grevy's, Plains and Mountain?	*Zebra*
6 What species of snake shares its name with a Cuban dance?	*Mamba*
7 What type of fish takes its name from the Portuguese meaning fish with teeth?	*Piranha*
8 Comprising 37 varieties, the toco is the largest species of which long-beaked bird?	*Toucan*
9 To which family of birds do canaries belong?	*Finch*
10 If an animal is polled what is removed?	*Horns*

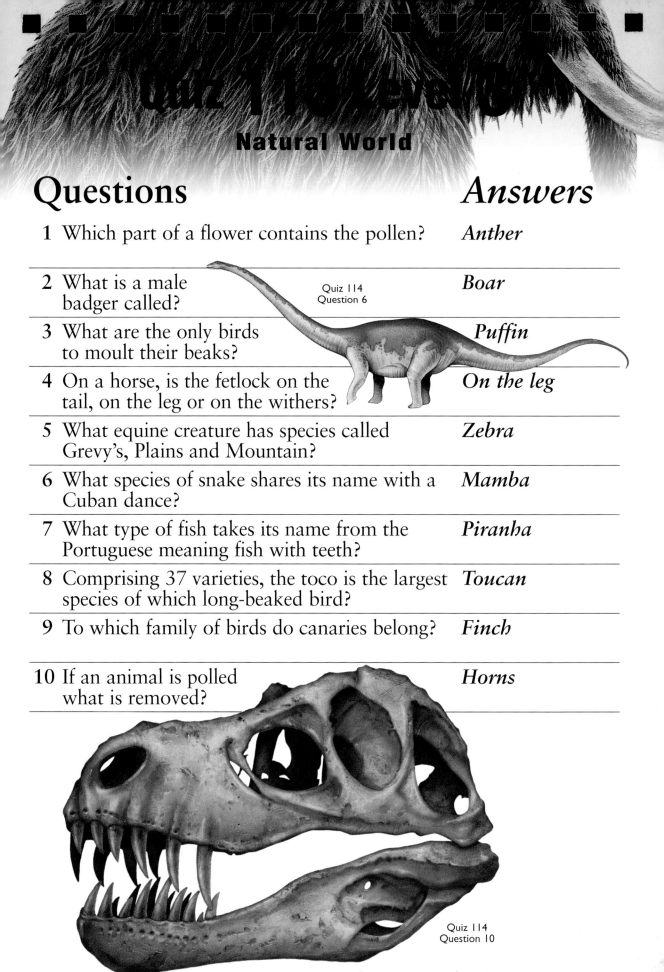

Quiz 114
Question 6

Quiz 114
Question 10

Questions

Answers

1 Which extinct relative of the elephant had varieties called Woolly and Imperial?

Mammoth

2 Was a brontosaurus a carnivore or a herbivore?

Quiz 113
Question 8

Herbivore

3 Who wrote the novel *Jurassic Park*?

Michael Crichton

4 What dinosaur had a name meaning three-horned face?

Triceratops

5 Is children's T.V. character Barney the Dinosaur red, purple or orange?

Purple

6 What dinosaur had a name meaning Earth shaking lizard?

Seismosaurus

7 The Smog Monster, King Kong and Monster Zero all faced which movie dinosaur?

Godzilla

8 Dinosaurs were mammals: true or false?

False (they were reptiles)

9 What does dinosaur literally mean in English: fearsome reptile, terrible lizard or giant beast?

Terrible lizard

10 The first fossil of which fearsome dinosaur was discovered in 1902 by Barnum Brown?

Tyrannosaurus Rex

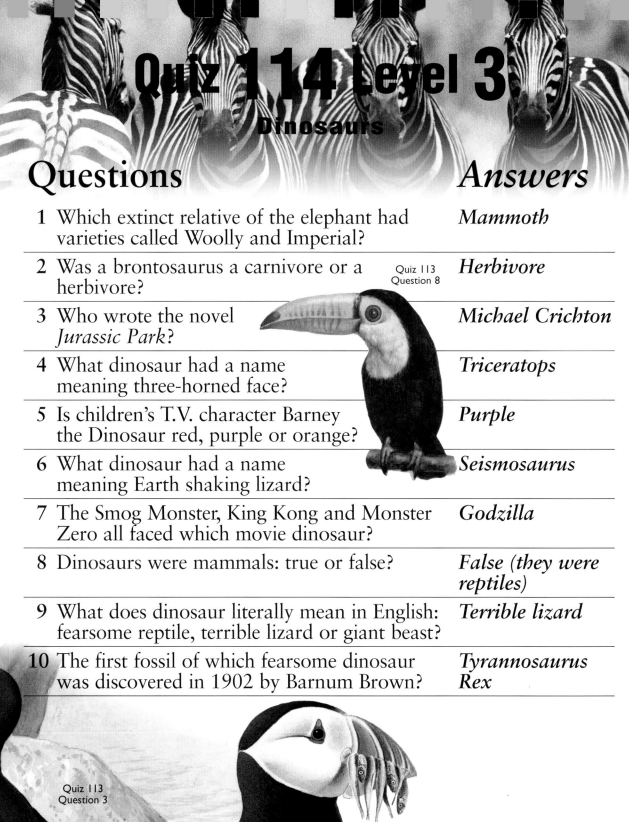

Quiz 113
Question 3

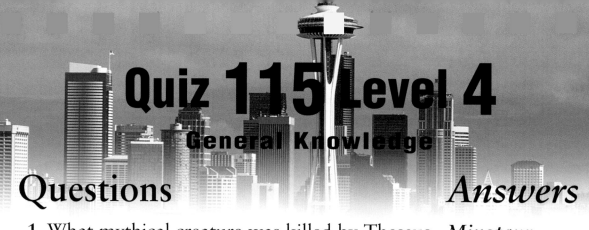

Quiz 115 Level 4

General Knowledge

Questions	Answers
1 What mythical creature was killed by Theseus in a labyrinth?	Minotaur
2 What is the largest state in the United States after Alaska and Texas?	California
3 What novel was Charles Dickens writing at the time of his death?	The Mystery of Edwin Drood
4 On a suit of armour what part of the body did a beaver protect?	Chin
5 How many white squares are found on a standard chessboard?	32
6 Who played the title role in the 1968 film *Inspector Clouseau*?	Alan Arkin
7 Who played Gregory in the film *Gregory's Girl*?	John Gordon Sinclair
8 What was the home port of Sir Francis Drake?	Plymouth
9 In what month is the Last Night of the Proms traditionally held?	September
10 What type of nuts are used to flavour marzipan?	Almonds

Quiz 116
Question 9

Quiz116
Question 1

Quiz 116 Level 4
General Knowledge

Questions	Answers
1 What are jumping cholla, barrel and organ pipe, species of?	*Cactus*
2 Which Monty Python star has the middle name of Marwood?	*John Cleese*
3 What is the lightest style of sherry?	*Manzanilla*
4 Which cartoon character owns a dog called Snowy?	*Tintin*
5 Which peak was the final resting place of Noah's Ark?	*Mount Ararat*
6 What is entomophobia the morbid fear of?	*Insects*
7 Where do Niles, Frasier and Daphne live?	*Seattle*
8 What was the title of Richard Burton's last film, which was also the year that he died?	1984
9 Which of the seven wonders of the ancient world was located on the island of Pharos?	*Alexandria Lighthouse*
10 Which city is served by Aldegrove Airport?	*Belfast*

Quiz 115
Question 10

Quiz 115
Question 5

Questions	Answers
1 Other than humans, what are the only other animals that can get leprosy?	*Armadillos*
2 Britain's largest is the Death Head, the world's largest is called the Hercules: what are they?	*Moths*
3 What material forms a shark's skeleton?	*Cartilage*
4 What animals have the largest teeth?	*Elephants (tusks are large incisors)*
5 Which seabird shares its name with a greedy person?	*Gannet*
6 What is a young otter called?	*Whelp*
7 Which animal has the largest brain?	*Sperm whale*
8 What is the name of the world's largest species of lizard?	*Komodo dragon*
9 Of all the rivers in the world, which contains the greatest amount of water?	*The Amazon*
10 To which fish family do goldfish belong?	*Carp*

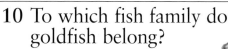

Quiz 118
Question 2

Quiz 118
Question 8

Quiz 118 Level 4
Natural World

Questions	Answers
1 Is a ladybird a beetle, an ant or a fly?	*Beetle*
2 What is the world's tallest ruminant?	*Giraffe*
3 After elephants what are the heaviest land mammals?	*Hippopotamus*
4 What timid burrowing animal has a name meaning earth pig?	*Aardvark*
5 What types of animals are the eland and impala?	*African antelopes*
6 What crime would you associate with the collective name for a group of crows?	*Murder*
7 Moray, black ribbon and leopard are all species of which sea creature?	*Eel*
8 What comical looking birds were named after the Spanish word for clown?	*Boobies*
9 Black Norfolk and Beltsville are both breeds of which tasty bird?	*Turkey*
10 If an animal is described as vermivorous, does it feed on rodents, insects or worms?	*Worms*

Quiz 117
Question 5

Quiz 117
Question 7

Quiz 119 Level 4
General Knowledge

Questions	Answers
1 What name is given to a person who displays a needless anxiety over their health?	*Hypochondriac*
2 Of which fictional girl's school was Millicent Fritton the headmistress?	*St. Trinian's*
3 Seville Queen and Kalamata are both types of what?	*Olives*
4 Is demography the study of maps, demonstrations or human population?	*Human population*
5 In which American city was the world's first telephone exchange established in 1878?	*Boston*
6 In which country would you find the towns of Hamilton, Palmerston North and Dunedin?	*New Zealand*
7 Who discovered the circulation of the blood?	*William Harvey*
8 Which British king reigned between 1547 and 1553?	*Edward VI*
9 What sitcom is set in the Bayview Retirement Home?	**Waiting For God**
10 What nationality were the Brothers Grimm?	*German*

Quiz 120
Question 10

Quiz 120
Question 5

Quiz 120 Level 4

General Knowledge

Questions	Answers
1 Who composed the violin concertos *The Four Seasons*?	*Vivaldi*
2 On which mountain did Moses receive the Ten Commandments from God?	*Mount Sinai*
3 Which famous literary traveller was the surgeon aboard a ship called *The Antelope*?	*Lemuel Gulliver*
4 What author did Anthony Hopkins play in the film *Shadowlands*?	*C.S. Lewis*
5 What is the state flower of Hawaii?	*Hibiscus*
6 What are the two most distant planets that Holst wrote pieces for in the *Planets Suite*?	*Neptune and Uranus*
7 Which rock star co-produced the film *Enigma*?	*Mick Jagger*
8 What is the nationality of a Helvetian?	*Swiss*
9 Which Motown icon married Syreeta Wright in 1970?	*Stevie Wonder*
10 What item of beachwear was invented by Louis Reard?	*The bikini*

Quiz 119
Question 8

Questions	Answers
1 Which Pope was canonized in the 20th century: Gregory XI, Pius X or John XV?	*Pius X*
2 Which English queen was executed in 1554 after ruling for only nine days?	*Lady Jane Grey*
3 Which Dickens novel was set against The Gordon Riots?	**Barnaby Rudge**
4 Who was Elizabeth I's first stepmother?	*Jane Seymour*
5 Who was the 35th president of the United States?	*John F. Kennedy*
6 Who conquered what is now central and southern Mexico, in the 16th century?	*Hernado Cortes*
7 Which pop group took their name from a Civil War group of men, led by John Lilburne?	*The Levellers*
8 What military organization was founded in 1831 by King Louis-Philippe?	*The Foreign Legion*
9 In the Bible who is the father-in-law of Moses: was it Jacob, Jethro or Joshua?	*Jethro*
10 Who commanded the defeated troops at the Battle of the Alamo?	*Colonel Will Travis*

Quiz 122
Question 2

Quiz 122
Question 3

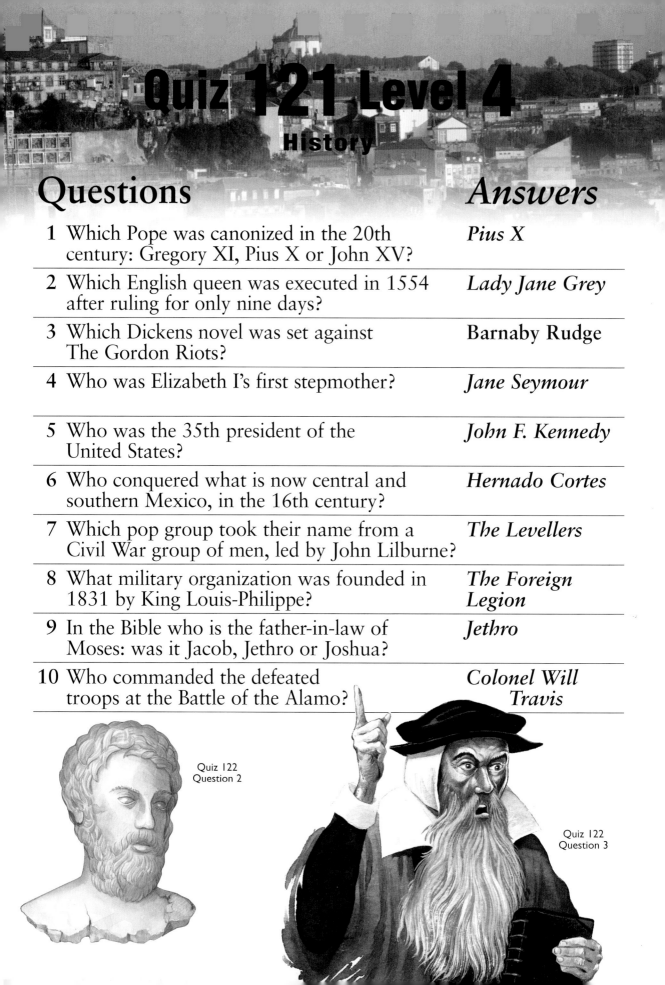

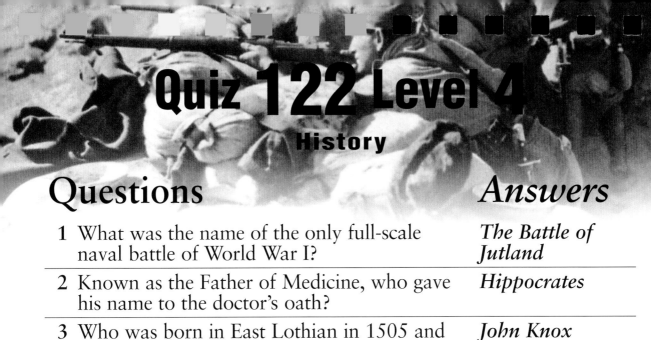

Quiz 122 Level 4

History

Questions	Answers
1 What was the name of the only full-scale naval battle of World War I?	*The Battle of Jutland*
2 Known as the Father of Medicine, who gave his name to the doctor's oath?	*Hippocrates*
3 Who was born in East Lothian in 1505 and founded Presbyterianism in Scotland?	*John Knox*
4 In the U.S. Civil War was The Battle of Bull Run fought in Texas, Arizona or Virginia?	*Virginia*
5 What name was given to the official bodyguards of Roman Emperors? Quiz 121 Question 5	*Praetorian Guards*
6 Which of Henry VIII's wives was Mary Tudor's mother?	*Catherine of Aragon*
7 When did the French Revolution end?	*1799*
8 Which is the world's oldest walled town?	*Jericho*
9 Name the American President who was assassinated in 1881.	*James Garfield*
10 In which African country is Tobruk, the scene of heavy fighting during World War II?	*Libya*

Quiz 121 Question 6

Quiz 123 Level 4
General Knowledge

Questions	Answers
1 Which Dickens novel featured the character of Silas Wegg?	Our Mutual Friend
2 Which country is the world's largest producer of tobacco?	China
3 What is the name of the resting place of the founder of the Persian Empire?	The Tomb of Cyrus
4 Is the zygomatic bone in the cheek, on the chin or in the nose?	The cheek
5 What is the Nikkei in Tokyo?	Stock Exchange
6 In which British city is Winsom Green Prison?	Birmingham
7 Of which American state was Bill Clinton the governor, before becoming President?	Arkansas
8 Is the Great Smoo Scotland's largest cave, waterfall or forest?	Cave
9 What is the name of the largest species of neotropical parrots?	Scarlet macaw
10 In mythology, what was the drink of the gods?	Nectar

Quiz 124
Question 1

Quiz 124
Question 10

Questions

Answers

#	Question	Answer
1	Which Gilbert & Sullivan operetta is also the title for a ruler in ancient Japan?	The Mikado
2	Which musical instrument derives its name from the Italian for soft and loud?	*Pianoforte*
3	Who wrote the novel *Chocolat*?	*Joanna Harris*
4	Cagliari is the capital of which Mediterranean island?	*Sardinia*
5	What is the nearest capital city to the equator?	*Quito (capital of Ecuador)*
6	Is euphoria a feeling of well-being or nausea?	*Well-being*
7	Pewter is an alloy of which two metals?	*Tin and lead*
8	The musical *The Boys From Syracuse* was based on which Shakespeare play?	A Comedy of Errors
9	*Constance Spry* and *Gertrude Jekyll* are varieties of which garden flower?	*Rose*
10	Which jazz musician was known as Satchmo?	*Louis Armstrong*

Quiz 123
Question 9

Quiz 123
Question 3

Quiz 125 Level 4

Science and Maths

Questions	Answers
1 What type of blood cells are responsible for transporting oxygen around the body?	*Red blood cells*
2 The renal artery supplies blood to which organ?	*Kidney*
3 What is a millionth of a metre called?	*Micron*
4 How many furlongs are there in 12 miles?	*96 (12x 8)*
5 Which element is the most toxic substance known to man?	*Plutonium*
6 Name the old measurement which was taken from the tip of the middle finger to the elbow?	*Cubit*
7 Which element has the lowest boiling point?	*Helium*
8 If an isosceles triangle has two angles of 70 degrees, what does the third angle measure?	*40 degrees*
9 What kind of magnifying instrument did the English scientist Edmund Culpeper develop?	*Microscope*
10 What are helium, neon, xenon, krypton and radon?	*Noble gasses*

Quiz 126
Question 5

Quiz 126
Question 8

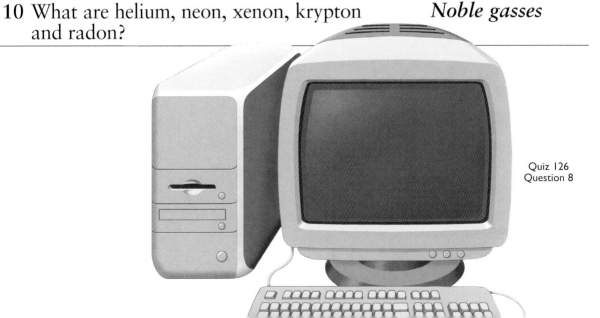

Quiz 126 Level 4
Science and Maths

Questions	Answers
1 What is the name of the branch of mechanics that deals with the motion and action of forces?	*Dynamics*
2 What name is given to the time of year, when night and day are of equal lengths?	*Equinox*
3 A supermarket sold 72 oranges from its stock of 96. What percentage did it sell?	*75%*
4 In the human body where would you find an oval window and a round window?	*In the ear*
5 In June 1965 astronaut Edward H. White II, became the first American to do what?	*Walk in space*
6 What is the medical name for the breastbone?	*Sternum*
7 What is the cube root of 343?	*Seven (7x7x7=343)*
8 What machines have R.O.M. and R.A.M.?	*Computers*
9 What are there 10,080 of in a week?	*Minutes*
10 How many feet are there in a mile?	*5,280*

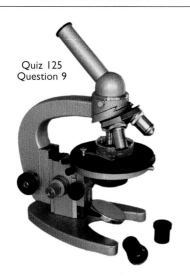

Quiz 125
Question 9

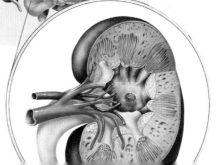

Quiz 125
Question 2

Quiz 127 Level 4
General Knowledge

Questions	Answers
1 What was the three-letter surname of the presiding judge in the O.J. Simpson murder trial?	*Ito*
2 In the United States what was banned from 1917 to 1933 by the 18th Amendment?	*Alcohol*
3 Who was the first singer to have a U.K. No. 1 hit with the song "Unchained Melody"?	*Jimmy Young*
4 Which is the only American city to be named after a British Prime Minister?	*Pittsburgh (William Pitt)*
5 What is the name of the parliament of the Isle of Man?	*Tynwald*
6 What was invented by the American Christopher Latham, in the 1860s?	*Typewriter*
7 What were Lord Byron's first names?	*George Gordon*
8 HMS *Resolution* was the name of the world's first what?	*Polaris submarine*
9 What does the medical condition D.V.T. stand for?	*Deep Vein Thrombosis*
10 What is the only marsupial native to North America?	*Opossum*

Quiz 128
Question 3

Quiz 128
Question 9

Quiz 128 Level 4
General Knowledge

Questions	Answers
1 The fruits of which plant are sold in America under the name of tuna?	*Prickly pear cactus*
2 Which singing voice comes between soprano and contralto?	*Mezzo-soprano*
3 Which American artist was nicknamed Jack the Dripper?	*Jackson Pollock*
4 From which chemical compound are mothballs made?	*Naphthalene*
5 What part of the body is also the name of a unit of currency in El Salvador?	Colon
6 Tom Selleck, Elliot Gould and Sarah Ferguson have all appeared in which U.S. sitcom?	Friends
7 According to the Old Testament, is the wife of Abraham called Sarah, Ruth or Esther?	*Sarah*
8 In which decade did Jack the Ripper terrorize the London district of Whitechapel?	*1880s*
9 Which birds were used by miners to detect poisonous gases in mines?	*The canary*
10 Where in the human body is bile stored?	*Gall bladder*

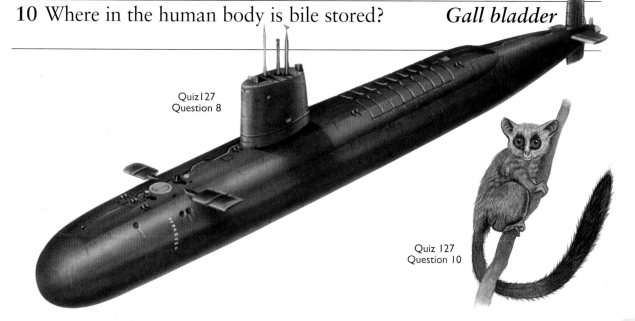

Quiz127
Question 8

Quiz 127
Question 10

Quiz 129 Level 4
Geography

Questions	Answers
1 In which U.S. city is the headquarters of the Coca Cola Company?	*Atlanta*
2 Which Swiss lake is sometimes referred to as The Lake of the Four Cantons?	*Lake Lucerne*
3 A picture of which building is depicted on the flag of Cambodia?	*The Temple of Angkor*
4 Which river flows through the city of Florence?	*River Arno*
6 What is the official state bird of Louisiana?	*Pelican*
7 Which capital city is served by Orly Airport?	*Paris*
5 Is Lusaka the capital of Zimbabwe, Zaire or Zambia?	*Zambia*
8 What is the most northerly of the Channel Islands?	*Alderney*
9 Which New Zealand city is nicknamed The Garden City?	*Christchurch*
10 Which country lies immediately south of Egypt?	*Sudan*

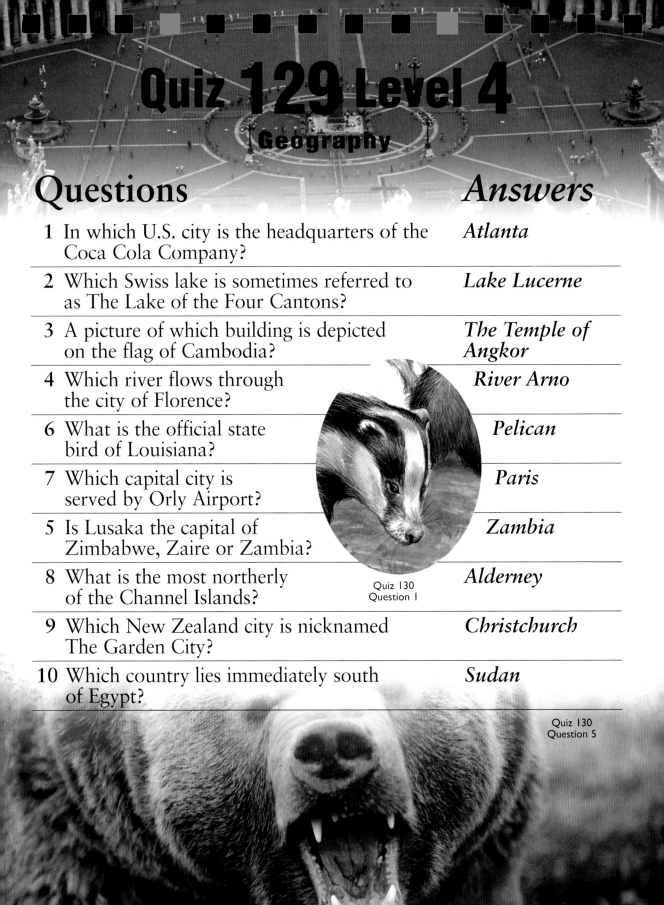

Quiz 130
Question 1

Quiz 130
Question 5

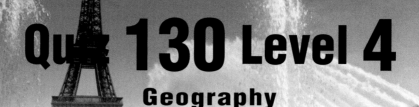

Quiz 130 Level 4

Geography

Questions	Answers
1 What type of animal is the official symbol of Bern, the capital of Switzerland?	*Badger*
2 What sea lies directly north of Poland? *Quiz 129 Question 6*	*Baltic Sea*
3 Ostia is the name of the port serving which capital city?	*Rome*
4 In which city is the headquarters of the Fiat car company?	*Turin*
5 What animal provides the nickname of the American state of Wisconsin?	*Bear*
6 Is the capital of Guyana called Georgetown, Victoria City or Albertville?	*Georgetown*
7 Fjordland National Park is in which country: Norway, New Zealand or Namibia?	*New Zealand*
8 Which capital city in the British Isles stands on the River Lagan?	*Belfast*
9 Which university was founded as The University of New Jersey in 1746?	*Princeton*
10 On which river does Baghdad stand?	*Tigris*

Quiz 129
Question 3

Questions	Answers
1 In what type of object would you find a rampart above an escapement?	*A clock*
2 Who slept in the teapot at the Mad Hatter's teaparty?	*The dormouse*
3 Is phlebitis the inflammation of the eye, a vein or the gums?	*A vein*
4 Which vitamin is found in citrus fruits?	*Vitamin C*
5 Which Alfred Hitchcock thriller was set mainly at Bodega Bay?	The Birds
6 What was the infamous London address of the murderer John Christie?	*10 Rillington Place*
7 What is the more common name for magnesium silicate?	*Talcum powder*
8 What type of passenger plane made its maiden flight in February 1969?	*Boeing 747*
9 In the 1950s which war did the Treaty of Panmunjon end?	*The Korean War*
10 Who was Roman Emperor when Jesus was crucified?	*Tiberius*

Quiz 132
Question 5

Quiz 132
Question 10

Quiz 132 Level 4

General Knowledge

Questions	Answers
1 If a substance is described as stannic, what metal does it contain?	*Tin*
2 How is the year 2000 written in Roman numerals?	*MM*
3 The year 2000 was the Chinese year of the what?	*The year of the Dragon*
4 Where in Utah is the headquarters of the Mormon religion?	*Salt Lake City*
5 Which are the only birds able to fly backwards?	*Hummingbirds*
6 What literary prize was won by Australian novelist Peter Carey in 2001?	*The Booker Prize*
7 In May 1994 the Channel Tunnel was officially opened at which English port?	*Folkestone*
8 Which pop singer named himself after the composer of the opera *Hansel & Gretel*?	*Engelbert Humperdinck*
9 Who was the first person to sail single-handed non-stop around the world?	*Robin Knox-Johnston*
10 On the body of a horse where is the dock?	*The tail*

Quiz 131
Question 1

Quiz 131
Question 2

Questions	Answers
1 What is the three-word motto of Gradgrind in the Dickens novel *Hard Times*?	*Facts, facts, facts*
2 What word is the opposite of the nautical term windward?	*Leeward*
3 If the body of an animal is described as lanate what is it covered in?	*Wool*
4 If canine equals dog what does vulpine equal?	*Fox*
5 Is a rotunda: a round domed building, a round musical instrument or a round jewelled brooch?	*A round domed building*
6 What English word derives from the Italian meaning little ball: balloon, ballot or ballet?	*Ballot*
7 What word of Japanese origin literally translates into English as harbour wave?	*Tsunami*
8 Who wrote the poem *Do Not Go Gentle Into That Good Night*?	*Dylan Thomas*
9 How does Anno Domini translate into English?	*In the year of our Lord*
10 Dendrophobia is the morbid fear of what?	*Trees*

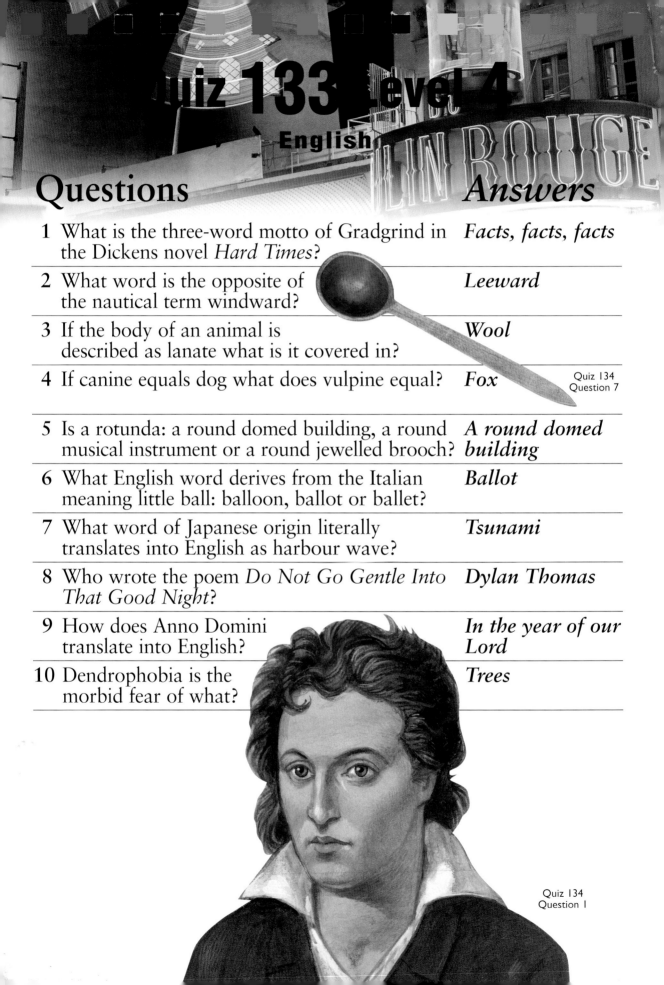

Quiz 134
Question 7

Quiz 134
Question 1

Quiz 134 Level 4
English

Questions	Answers
1 Which author, born in 1792, wrote the poems *Ode To The West Wind* and *To A Skylark*?	*Percy Shelley*
2 What does the E stand for in the food additives known as E numbers?	*European*
3 What C word is the name given to an assembly of Cardinals?	*Conclave*
4 What is the literal English translation of the Italian word *veto*?	*I forbid*
5 In the novel *1984*, what language are the authorities trying to introduce?	*Newspeak*
6 What S word is the name given to the highest order of angels in the celestial hierarchy?	*Seraphim*
7 Complete the old saying "He who sups with the Devil should have a long .."?	*Spoon*
8 Bathsheba Everdene is the heroine of which novel by Thomas Hardy?	**Far From The Madding Crowd**
9 What is unusual about the word facetious?	*All the vowels appear in order*
10 The name of which Parisian night club translates into English as red windmill?	*Moulin Rouge*

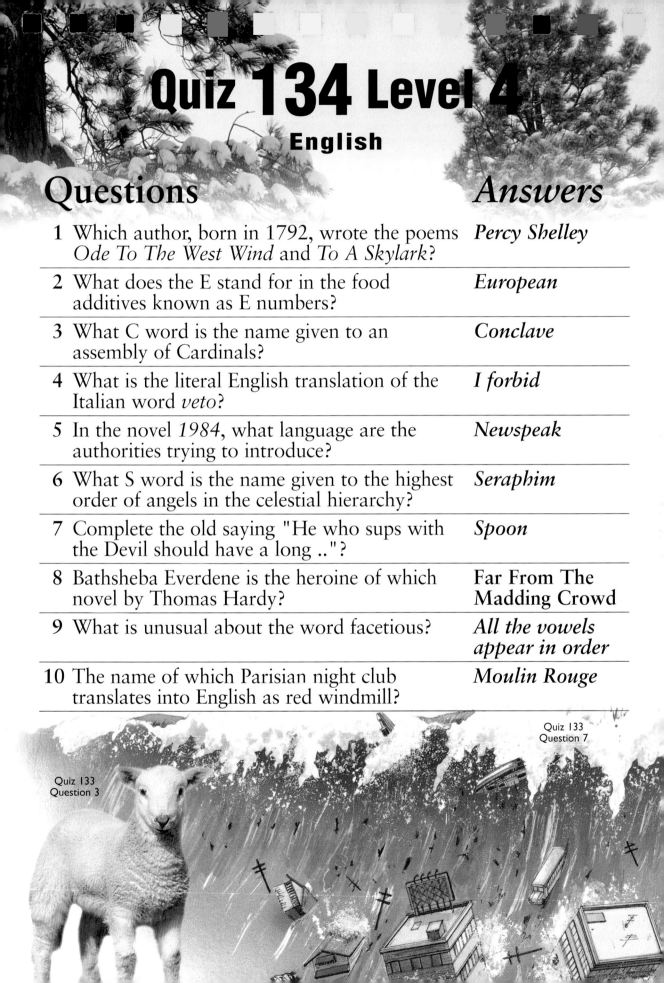

Quiz 133
Question 7

Quiz 133
Question 3

Quiz 135 Level 4

General Knowledge

Questions	Answers
1 Which planet is named after the Roman messenger of the gods?	Mercury
2 In which 2001 film does Sandra Bullock play an undercover cop in a beauty contest?	Miss Congeniality
3 Which Russian town was the site of a nuclear disaster in April 1986?	Chernobyl
4 In the time of Edward VIII, the old halfpenny coin depicted which ship on the tail side?	The Golden Hind
5 What is the world's largest rodent?	Capybara
6 What name is given to the pupa of a butterfly?	Chrysalis
7 Which American President introduced the new deal?	Franklin D. Rossevelt
8 By what title is Richard John Bingham more notoriously known?	Lord Lucan
9 Robinson and Dancy are both varieties of which fruit?	Tangerine
10 In 1897, was the Women's Institute established in Canada, Wales or South Africa?	Canada

Quiz 136
Question 7

Questions	Answers
1 Beefsteak, Brandywine and Bull's Heart are all varieties of what edible object?	*Tomato*
2 What ship was first launched in Nova Scotia in 1870 and was originally named Amazon?	**Marie Celeste**
3 A sky with altocumulus clouds shares its name with what type of fish?	*Mackerel*
4 Who is the patron saint of hopeless causes?	*St. Jude*
5 Was Princess Anne born in 1950, 1951 or 1952?	*1950*
6 In which year did the U.S. Civil War start?	*1861*
7 What is laver bread made from?	*Seaweed*
8 Which of the seven wonders of the world was built to honour the Greek goddess of hunting?	*The Temple of Artemis*
9 "The course of true love never did run smooth" is a quote from which Shakespeare play?	**A Midsummer Night's Dream**
10 Did the Egyptian God Anubis, have the head of a cobra, jackal or a falcon?	*Jackal*

Quiz 135
Question 4

Quiz 135
Question 5

Quiz 137 Level 4
T.V. and Film

Questions	Answers
1 Which Robert Redford film, based on a true story, was set at Wakefield Prison Farm?	Brubaker
2 Who played Porter in the movie *Payback*?	*Mel Gibson*
3 Which of The Monkees also appeared in *Coronation Street*?	*Davy Jones*
4 Which sitcom features the character of Nurse Gladys Emanuel?	Open All Hours
5 Which stetson-wearing actor was born Leonard Slye?	*Roy Rogers*
6 In which film did Helen Mirren play Queen Charlotte?	The Madness of King George
7 Who was the first actress to win four Best Actress Oscars?	*Katharine Hepburn*
8 What kind of animal was Jimmy Stewart's companion in the film *Harvey*?	*A giant rabbit*
9 Which sport features in the film *The Waterboy*?	*American Football*
10 What was the screen name of Norma Jean Baker?	*Marilyn Monroe*

Quiz 138
Question 1

Quiz 138
Question 5

Questions

Answers

1 Who played the title role of Harry Lime in the film *The Third Man*? — *Orson Wells*

2 In the T.V. drama *Upstairs, Downstairs* what is the name of the family that live upstairs? — *Bellamy*

3 Reckless was the name of the pet dog of which T.V. family? — The Waltons

4 Which sport featured in the 1985 film *American Flyers*? — *Cycling*

5 Which profession is represented by the T.V. series *N.Y.P.D. Blue*? — *U.S. police force*

6 Who played Captain John Miller in the film *Saving Private Ryan*? — Tom Hanks

7 In which 1967 film did Paul Newman eat 50 eggs in one hour? — Cool Hand Luke

8 What is the surname of Kevin the teenager in *The Harry Enfield Show*? Quiz 137 Question 10 — *Patterson*

9 Which 1953 film opens with Doris Day singing "The Deadwood Stage"? — Calamity Jane

10 In which city is *Cagney and Lacey* set? Quiz 137 Question 8 — *New York*

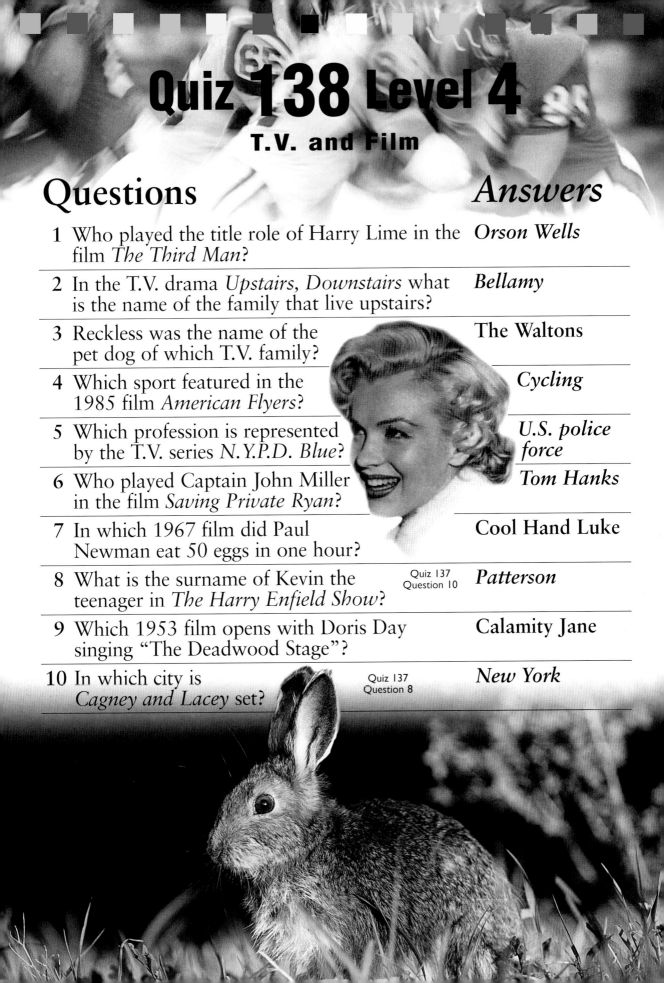

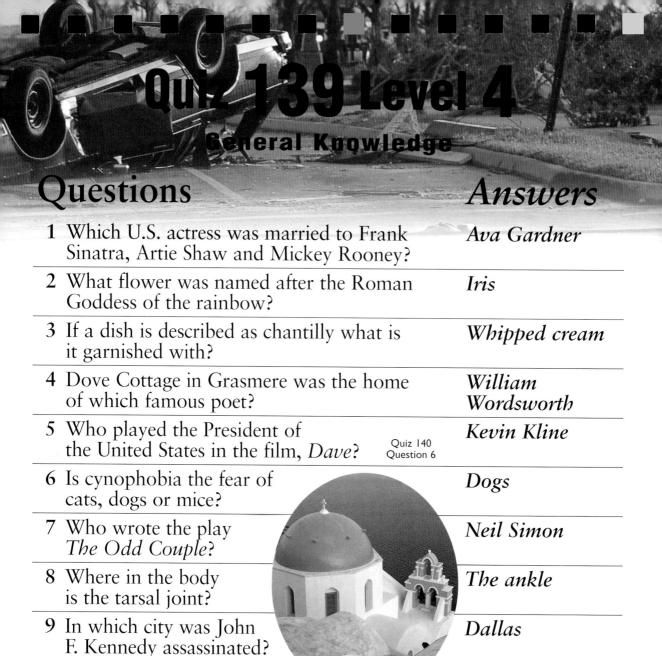

Quiz 139 Level 4
General Knowledge

Questions	Answers
1 Which U.S. actress was married to Frank Sinatra, Artie Shaw and Mickey Rooney?	*Ava Gardner*
2 What flower was named after the Roman Goddess of the rainbow?	*Iris*
3 If a dish is described as chantilly what is it garnished with?	*Whipped cream*
4 Dove Cottage in Grasmere was the home of which famous poet?	*William Wordsworth*
5 Who played the President of the United States in the film, *Dave*?	*Kevin Kline*
6 Is cynophobia the fear of cats, dogs or mice?	*Dogs*
7 Who wrote the play *The Odd Couple*?	*Neil Simon*
8 Where in the body is the tarsal joint?	*The ankle*
9 In which city was John F. Kennedy assassinated?	*Dallas*
10 Who invented the dynamo?	*Michael Faraday*

Quiz 140
Question 6

Quiz 140
Question 7

Quiz 140 Level 4

General Knowledge

Questions	Answers
1 In which present day country is the site of the Hanging Gardens of Babylon?	*Iraq*
2 Which member of the British royal family is the Chancellor of Cambridge University?	*Prince Charles*
3 What sea creature is made up of 95% water, has no heart, brain, bones, eyes, gills or blood?	*Jellyfish*
4 In which 1999 film does Denzel Washington play boxer Rubin Carter?	**The Hurricane**
5 In which river did the Pied Piper drown the rats of Hamelin?	*Weser*
6 Which European country is also known as the Hellenic Republic?	*Greece*
7 What Z word is the name of pyramidal mounds of the ancient Mesopotamians?	*Ziggurat*
8 Which teenager recorded the album *Voice Of An Angel* in 1999?	*Charlotte Church*
9 Founded in 1903, what is the name of England's first garden city?	*Letchworth*
10 What was Buddy Holly's real first name?	*Charles*

Quiz 139
Question 2

Quiz 139
Question 10

Quiz ¡41 Level 4
Sport

Questions	Answers
1 What name is given to metal spikes hammered into rock as anchors?	*Pitons (pins and pegs)*
2 What kind of race has categories called pairs, long track, teams and individual?	*Speedway*
3 From which country does the sport of pelota originate?	*Spain*
4 Which European capital city hosted the Winter Olympics in the 20th Century?	*Oslo*
5 How wide is the balance beam in women's gymnastics?	*10 cm/4 inches*
6 In an Olympic discus competition, how many throws is each contestant allowed?	*Six*
7 What type of racing was founded in 1947 at Daytona Beach?	*NASCAR*
8 In cycling who wears the yellow jersey?	*The race leader*
9 Which Panamanian boxer was nicknamed Hands of Stone?	*Roberto Duran*
10 In which game do you bulley off?	*Hockey*

Quiz 142
Question 7

Quiz 142
Question 2

Quiz 142 Level 4

Sport

Questions	Answers
1 In 1985, which unseeded player was crowned Wimbledon Men's Singles Champion?	*Boris Becker*
2 In which sport would a mashie niblick be used?	*Golf*
3 In skeleton tobogganing, does the rider travel feet first or head first?	*Head first*
4 What nationality is tennis star Mark Philippoussis?	*Australian*
5 In the U.K. which shooting season starts on August 12 and ends on December 10?	*Grouse shooting*
6 In which sport is the Swaythling Cup a major competition?	*Table tennis*
7 On a yacht what are halyards: sails, ropes or anchors?	*Ropes*
8 In 1996 which nation were crowned World Ice Hockey Champions?	*Czech Republic*
9 In judo if the referee says *Hajime!*, what should you do?	*Start fighting*
10 Which course stages the Irish Derby in horse racing?	*The Curragh*

Quiz 141
Question 7

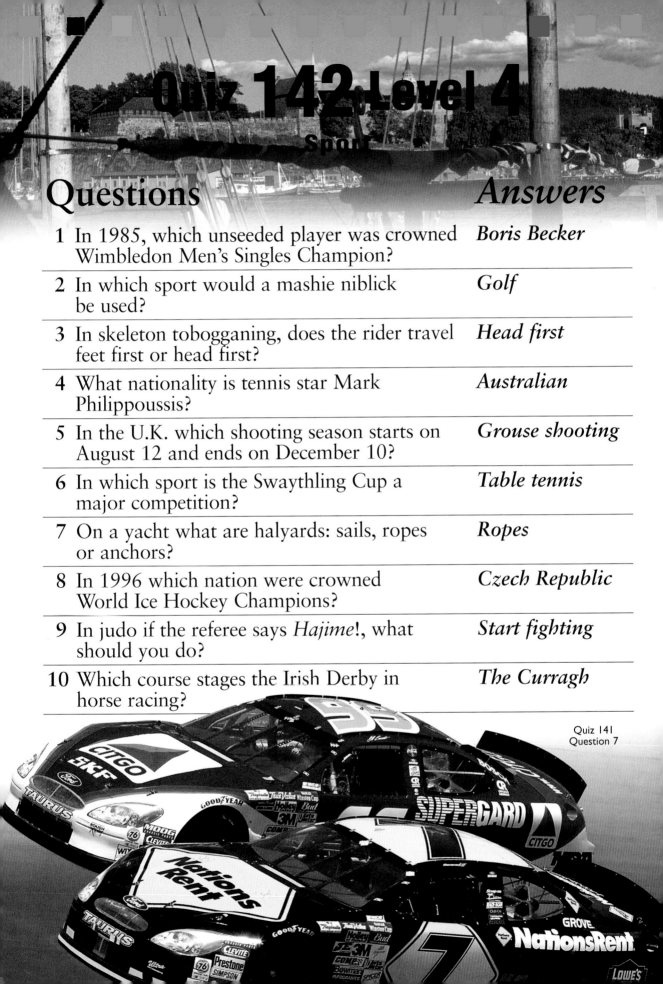

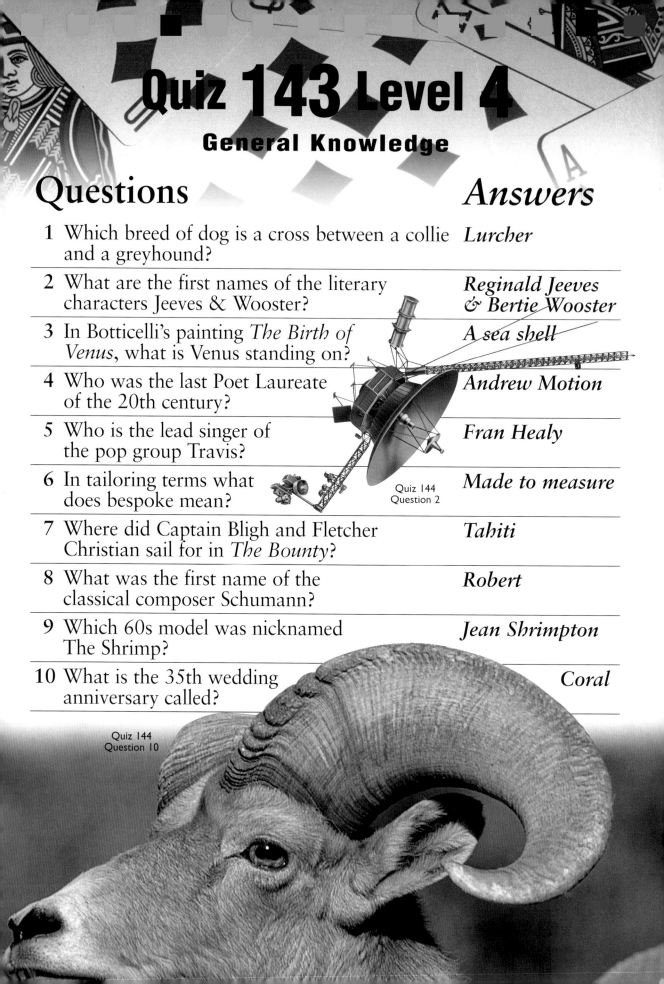

Quiz 143 Level 4
General Knowledge

Questions	Answers
1 Which breed of dog is a cross between a collie and a greyhound?	*Lurcher*
2 What are the first names of the literary characters Jeeves & Wooster?	*Reginald Jeeves & Bertie Wooster*
3 In Botticelli's painting *The Birth of Venus*, what is Venus standing on?	*A sea shell*
4 Who was the last Poet Laureate of the 20th century?	*Andrew Motion*
5 Who is the lead singer of the pop group Travis?	*Fran Healy*
6 In tailoring terms what does bespoke mean?	*Made to measure*
7 Where did Captain Bligh and Fletcher Christian sail for in *The Bounty*?	*Tahiti*
8 What was the first name of the classical composer Schumann?	*Robert*
9 Which 60s model was nicknamed The Shrimp?	*Jean Shrimpton*
10 What is the 35th wedding anniversary called?	*Coral*

Quiz 144
Question 2

Quiz 144
Question 10

Quiz 144 Level 4

General Knowledge

Questions	Answers
1 Boston, Napoleon, Pope Joan and Piquet are all the names of what?	*Card games*
2 Which NASA spacecraft flew past Uranus in 1986?	*Voyager 2*
3 Which glands in the body make white blood cells?	*Lymph glands*
4 What is the more common name for dyspepsia?	*Indigestion*
5 Robben Island is in the bay of which African city?	*Cape Town*
6 Who directed the film *Cry Freedom*?	*Richard Attenborough*
7 In Japan where on the body is a *tobi* worn?	*On the foot (it is a sock)*
8 The masked hero Zorro took his name from the Spanish word for which animal?	*Fox*
9 Is the literal translation of *Homo Sapiens*, ape man, wise man or upright man?	*Wise man*
10 What star sign encompasses the end of March and the beginning of April?	*Aries (the Ram)*

Quiz 143
Question 3

Quiz 143
Question 10

Questions	Answers
1 What is the common name for the wild cat known as an ounce?	*Snow leopard*
2 The adjective cervine refers to which of the following animals: deer, cats or beavers?	*Deer*
3 Other than a walrus, what is the only sea creature that possesses an ivory tusk?	*Narwhal*
4 What slow-moving, winged insect, has varieties called Chinese and Carolina?	*Praying mantis*
5 Which London park houses London Zoo?	*Regents Park*
6 How many feet do snails have?	*One*
7 From which animal is nutria fur obtained?	*Coypu*
8 Which Disney character was named after the Swahili word for lion?	*Simba*
9 Which mammals native to Madagascar, have species called ring-tailed and Indri?	*Lemur*
10 What bird lays the smallest eggs?	*Hummingbird*

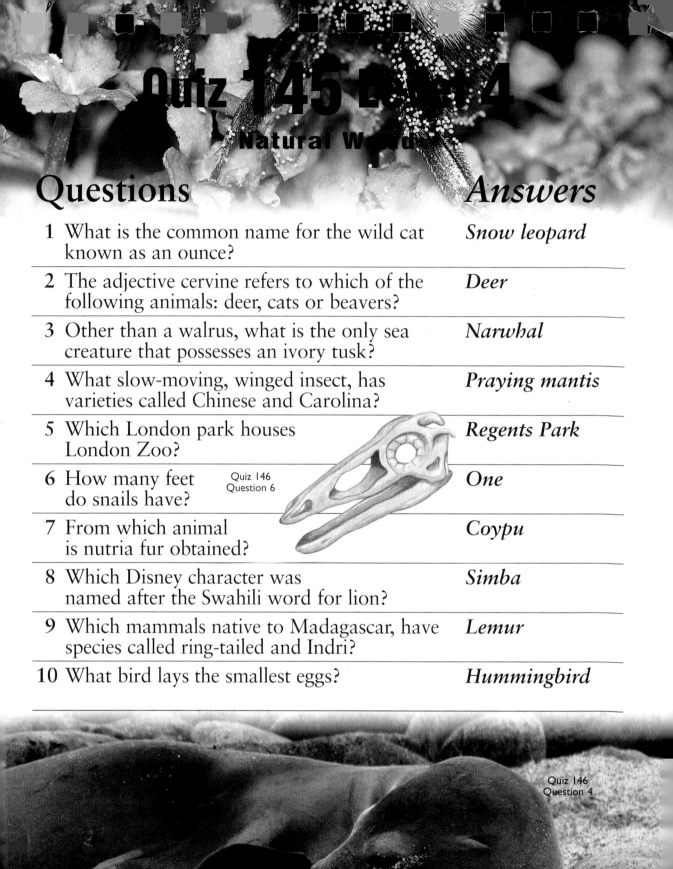

Quiz 146
Question 6

Quiz 146
Question 4

Quiz 146 Level 4
English

Questions	Answers
1 Alphabetically which is the first book of the Bible?	*Acts*
2 If an object is described as cordate, what part of the body is it shaped like?	*A heart*
3 What is the home state of the literary character Tom Sawyer?	*Mississippi*
4 A seal is a pinniped. What does this mean?	*It has flippers*
5 *The Roman Hat Mystery* marked the literary debut of which detective?	*Ellery Queen*
6 Animal or plant remains preserved in rock are known as what?	*Fossils*
7 What do you call the study of armorial bearings?	*Heraldry*
8 What is the name given to a long-handled pair of glasses?	*Lorgnette*
9 What number is indicated by the prefix tetra?	*Four*
10 Is apiphobia the fear of gorillas, tigers or bees?	*Bees*

Quiz 145
Question 7

Quiz 145
Question 9

Geography

Questions	Answers
1 Other than New York, which city has an airport named after John F. Kennedy?	*La Paz (Bolivia)*
2 From which English city did Concorde make its maiden flight?	*Bristol*
3 On which river does the city of Geneva stand?	*Rhone*
4 The Gulf of Bothnia lies between which two North European countries?	*Finland and Sweden*
5 Shah Jahan is best known for building which Indian monument? Quiz 148 Question 6	*The Taj Mahal*
6 The Samoyed breed of dog originated in which country?	*Russia*
7 Which Indian city is served by Dum Dum Airport?	*Calcutta*
8 Which cathedral in south Germany has the world's tallest church spire?	*Ulm Cathedral*
9 Tehran is the capital of which country?	*Iran*
10 Which Flavian amphitheatre was built in the gardens of Nero's palace?	*Colosseum*

Quiz 148 Question 9

Quiz **148** Level **4**

Sport

Questions	Answers
1 In which sport do the Oxford Cheetahs compete?	*Ice hockey*
2 In which Italian city is the San Siro football stadium?	*Milan*
3 At which British sporting venue would you find the Valley of Sin?	*St. Andrew's golf course*
4 Which country has more polo clubs than any other?	*Argentina*
5 First raced around the Isle of Wight in 1851, this competition became known as what?	*The America's Cup*
6 A game of what starts at the south stake?	*Croquet*
7 How many events are there in the heptathlon?	*Seven*
8 In which sport would a competitor land in the telemark position?	*Ski jumping*
9 What is the national sport of Japan?	*Sumo wrestling*
10 What is a velodrome?	*Cycle racing track*

Quiz 147
Question 8

Quiz 147
Question 9

Questions	Answers
1 Which famous composer was played by Tom Hulce in a 1984 Oscar winning film?	*Wolfgang Amadeus Mozart*
2 In which film did Marlon Brando say "I coulda been a contender"?	On The Waterfront
3 Is Grandpa Simpson called Isaac, Abraham or Jacob?	*Abraham*
4 What is the name of Bruce Wayne's butler in *Batman*?	*Alfred*
5 What was the last film that James Dean starred in?	Giant
6 In the film *Romancing The Stone*, what kind of animal did the writer Joan Wilder own?	*Iguana*
7 Which actor plays the brother-in-law of Hyacinth Bucket in *Keeping Up Appearances*?	*Jeffrey Hughes*
8 Which Hollywood actor, star of the film *Some Like It Hot*, died in 2001 aged 76?	*Jack Lemmon*
9 Who plays the character of Molly Brown in the 1997 film *Titanic*?	*Kathy Bates*
10 What instrument plays the theme music to the film O Brother, Where Art Thou?	*The banjo*

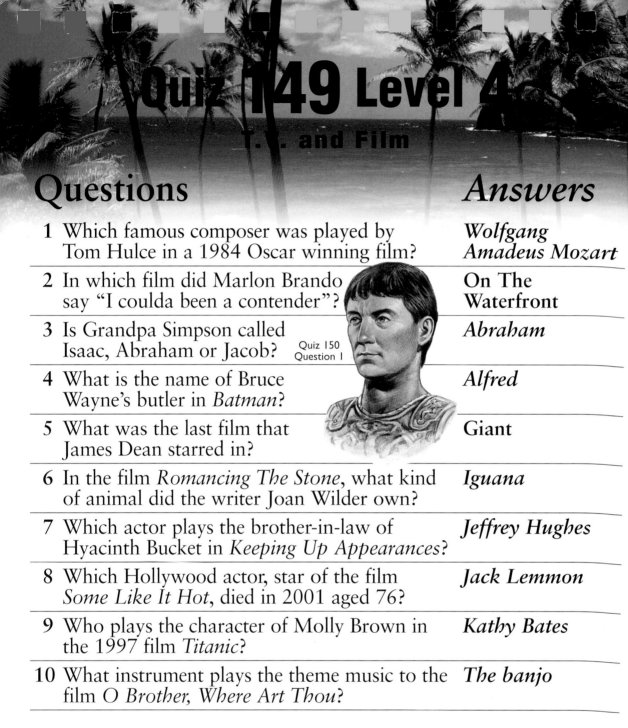

Quiz 150
Question 1

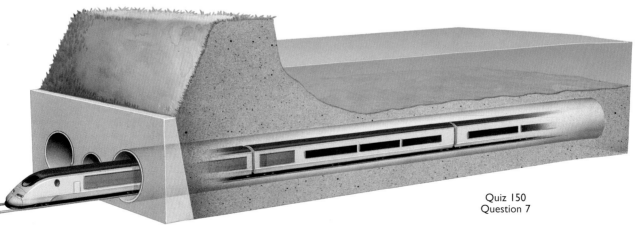

Questions

Answers

1	In 63BC who became the first Roman Emperor?	*Augustus Caesar*
2	Who was the leader of the Gunpowder Plot?	*Robert Catesby*
3	In which century was Michaelangelo born?	*15th century*
4	In which present day U.S. state was Captain James Cook killed by natives?	*Hawaii*
5	In which year did the Gulf War start?	*1990*
6	What connects the monarchs Richard II, Edward II and Edward VIII?	*They all abdicated*
7	What did Queen Elizabeth II and President Mitterand officially open in May 1994?	*The Channel Tunnel*
8	Did Vikings first invade Britain in the 7th, 8th or 9th century?	*The 8th century*
9	What was the name of the Earl of Tyrone, who was a sworn enemy of Elizabeth I?	*Hugh O'Neil*
10	What does the B stand for in the name of former U.S. President, Lyndon B. Johnson?	*Baines*

Quiz 149
Question 1

Quiz 149
Question 10

Questions   ## Answers

1 Battledore is the old name for what piece of sporting equipment? — *Badminton racket*

2 16 Lancaster Gate, London, is the address of which sporting organization? — *Football Association*

3 What sport is played by the Sheffield Sharks? — *Basketball*

4 In which sport are players awarded Brownlow Medals? — *Australian Rules Football*

5 Which sport combines cross-country skiing with smallbore rifle shooting? — *Biathlon*

6 What sport would you be watching at Happy Valley in Hong Kong? — *Horse racing*

7 Was the first city to host the modern Summer Olympics: Paris, Rome or London? — *Paris*

8 How many substitutes is a water polo team allowed to make: two, three or four? — *Four*

9 If I were to serve, dig, spike or set, what sport would I be playing? — *Volleyball*

10 Which Soviet leader officially opened the 1980 Moscow Olympics? — *Leonid Brezhnev*

Quiz 152
Question 10